Multi-Level HOME PLANS

GARLINGHOUSE

Library of Congress No. 88-82936

ISBN: 0-938708-23-6

Canadian orders should be submitted to:

The Garlinghouse Company, Inc.
20 Cedar Street North
Kitchener, Ontario N2H 2W8
(519) 743-4169

TABLE OF CONTENTS

Country Living

No. 26860

The design of this comfortable home says country living at its best. Constructed of energy-efficient wood for beauty and warmth, this home offers room for a growing family at an affordable price. The master bedroom and bath are on the second floor with a small deck. Two bedrooms and a bath are separated from the living area on the main level by the foyer. The living room and family room both have their own deck. A large eat-in kitchen and separate dining room complete this energy conscious design.

First floor — 1,434 sq. ft.
Second floor — 361 sq. ft.
Basement — 911 sq. ft.
Garage — 494 sq. ft.

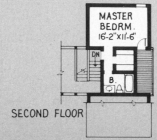

SECOND FLOOR

No. 26860

A Karl Kreeger Design

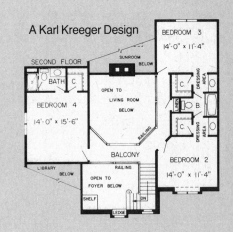

SECOND FLOOR

BATH C

BEDROOM 4
14'-0" x 15'-6"

SUNROOM
BELOW

OPEN TO
LIVING ROOM
BELOW

RAILING

BEDROOM 3
14'-0" x 11'-4"

C DRESSING
AREA

LINEN B.

C DRESSING
AREA

BALCONY

LIBRARY
BELOW

RAILING

OPEN TO
FOYER BELOW

SHELF

LEDGE

DN

BEDROOM 2
14'-0" x 11'-4"

Updated Country Manor House

No. 20071

No. 20071

Take advantage of a southern exposure and save on energy costs in this beautiful family tudor. Heat is stored in the floor of the sun room, adjoining the living and breakfast rooms. When the sun goes down, close the french doors and light a fire in the massive fireplace. State-of-the-art energy saving is not the only modern convenience in this house. You'll love the balcony overlooking the soaring two-story foyer and living room. In addition to providing great views, the balcony links the upstairs bedrooms. You're sure to enjoy the island kitchen, centrally located between formal and informal dining rooms. And, you'll never want to leave the luxurious master suite, with its double vanities and step-up whirlpool.

First floor — 2,186 sq. ft.
Second floor — 983 sq. ft.
Basement — 2,186 sq. ft.
Garage — 704 sq. ft.

3

Garden Room Dominates Plan

No. 28018

A 2-story passive solar home designed for the outdoor enthusiast. The upper level shows two bedrooms and a bath on the east side and a studio and storage area on the west. A balcony overlooks the garden room on the main floor which also shows a large master bedroom with private bath and large walk-in closet, living room, formal dining area, kitchen and pantry. A guest bath and a den completes the floor plan. Direct solar gain through the south facing garden room windows provides much of the heating requirements for this home.

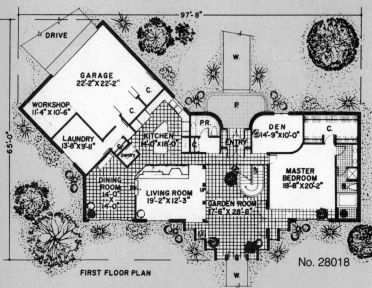

FIRST FLOOR PLAN

No. 28018

First floor — 2,527 sq. ft.
Second floor — 1,115 sq. ft.
Garage, workshop — 884 sq. ft.

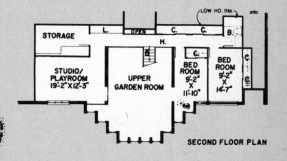

SECOND FLOOR PLAN

Step Down to the Living Room

No. 26880

This all-wood dramatic home features a
large living room that is one step down from
the dining room and entry way. Two bedrooms share a bath, while the master bedroom shows a fireplace, sitting room and
private bath. The large deck is accessible
from both the master suite and the breakfast
room. The upper level houses the game
room with its own deck. Thick cedar shingles add interest to the roof, and the cedar
siding requires little maintenance. This
home would be an asset wherever it was
built.

First floor — 2,357 sq. ft.
Second floor — 271 sq. ft.

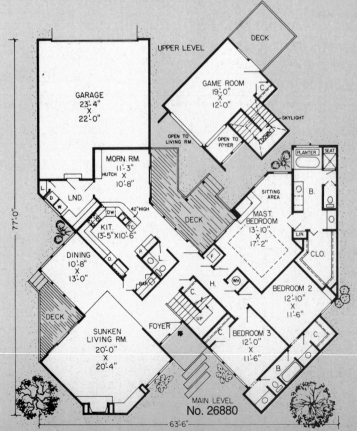

UPPER LEVEL

DECK

GARAGE
23'-4"
X
22'-0"

GAME ROOM
19'-0"
X
12'-0"

SKYLIGHT

OPEN TO
LIVING RM.

OPEN TO
FOYER

DOWN

MORN. RM.
11'-3"
X
10'-8"

HUTCH

LND.

PLANTER   SEAT

B.

SITTING
AREA

DECK

MAST.
BEDROOM
13'-10"
X
17'-2"

LIN

CLO.

KIT.
13'-5"X10'-6"

DW

42"HIGH

DINING
10'-8"
X
13'-0"

BAR

P

F

BEDROOM 2
12'-10"
X
11'-6"

H.

WH

C.

UP

C.

BEDROOM 3
12'-0"
X
11'-6"

C.

DECK

SUNKEN
LIVING RM.
20'-0"
X
20'-4"

FOYER

B.

77'-0"

63'-6"

MAIN LEVEL
No. 26880

Spacious and Airy

No. 19819

This charming 3-bedroom home displays an openness that paves the way for a variety of life styles. The upper level loft shows a den and game room with storage space between. Both overlook the living areas below. The master suite has access to a greenhouse as well as the possibility of installing stairs to the den above, providing a private retreat. The kitchen and dining area open to the large family room. A fireplace is featured in both the living room and the family room. A patio separates the garage from the house. The unusual design of the windows and the possibilities of personal design all contribute to the delightful livability of this family oriented home.

First floor — 1,438 sq. ft.
Loft — 550 sq. ft.
Garage — 484 sq. ft.

UPPER LEVEL

OPEN TO BEDRM

DEN
12x11

OPEN TO FAMILY

STOR

GAME RM
14 x11

DN

OPEN TO LIVING

39'-6"

GREEN-HOUSE

BEDRM
15x12

37'-0"

FAMILY
17x12

BEDRM
9½x11½

BATH

KIT
8x11

DINING
9x11

ENTRY

BEDRM
12½x9

PATIO

UP

LIVING
17x12

GARAGE
21x21

MAIN LEVEL

No. 19819

Luxury Home with Oriental Flair

No. 20006

From its impressive facade to its smallest details, this cut stone two-story home expresses luxury. On the first floor a dramatic entry is given by a large foyer and sweeping, curving stairs beyond. The living room, of which the rear half rises two stories, and a den are located further beyond the stairs. Both the living room and den open onto a rear balcony which overlooks the patio and covered pool. A built-in bar is included in the den. The master suite with two baths and numerous closets, a large library, project room, another half bath and a file room lie to the right of the entry. On the other side are a formal dining room, a kitchen and breakfast room. The breakfast room opens onto a delightful screened porch at the back which gives access to the deck and is only a few feet from the pool. A utility room with another half bath and a three car garage complete this level. A sauna, dressing rooms and half bath are found in the basement. On the second floor are three bedrooms, two baths and two storage rooms. Two balconies on this level overlook the living room.

First floor — 3,975 sq. ft.
Second floor — 2,205 sq. ft.
Basement — 3,975 sq. ft.
Garage — 753 sq. ft.

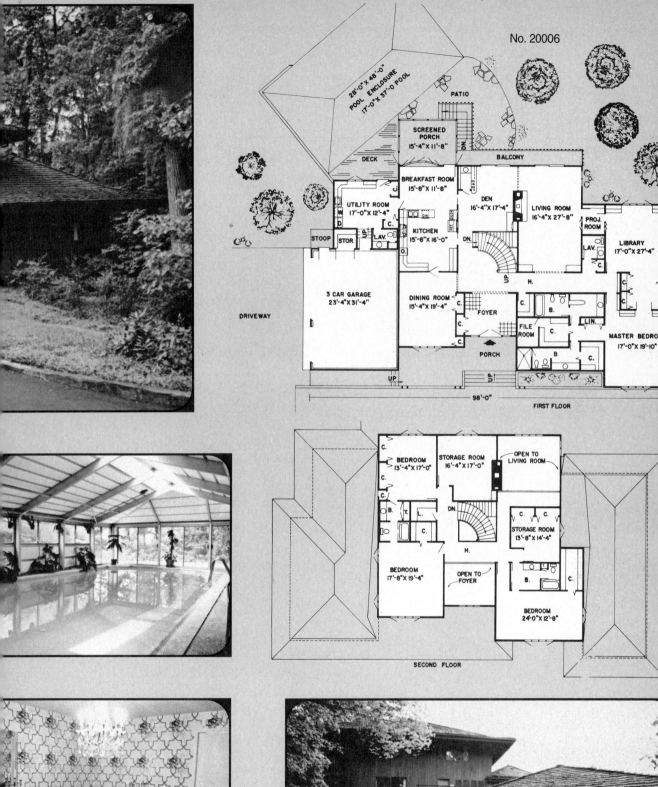

Ornate Windows Featured

No. 26782

Charm is found inside and out in this modified Victorian-style solar design. Cedar shakes, narrow horizontal siding, an ornate window arrangement and varying roof angles add to the exterior appeal. Inside, an airlock entry, heat-circulating fireplace in the great room, and a two-story greenhouse with concrete and brick floor for heat storage combine to produce an energy efficient design. A spacious combination formal dining-great room highlight the lower level. The kitchen lies snuggled between a multi-purpose room and causal eating area. A master suite, additional bath, bedroom and bedroom-den occupy the second level. Openings and windows between second level rooms and upper portions of the foyer, great room, and greenhouse enhance air circulation. An extra large double garage completes the design.

Upper level — 1,078 sq. ft.
Lower level — 1,108 sq. ft.
Garage — 618 sq. ft.
Deck — 240 sq. ft.
Greenhouse — 196 sq. ft.

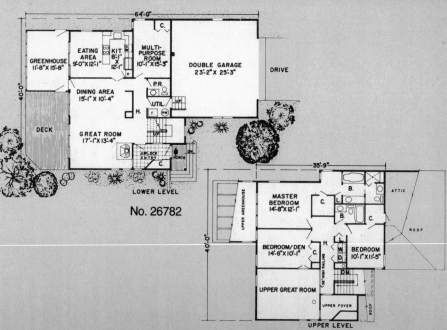

Accent on Luxury

No. 10655

Your houseguests may never want to leave this updated 5 bedroom manor home. Sturdy brick construction and elegant detailing — such as recessed octagonal ceilings, built in cabinets, shelves, and pantry — make this a special place. Extra amenities include the hexagonal sunny breakfast room with access to the deck, two powder rooms, guest bedroom, and full bath all on the first floor. The soaring two story foyer, flanked by the library and dining room, offers a view of the curved staircase and a glimpse of the wood-beamed great room beyond. Walk up the stairs and find a huge master bedroom suite with skylit bath, along with three more bedrooms and two full baths.

First floor — 2,526 sq. ft.
Second floor — 2,062 sq. ft.
Basement — 2,493 sq. ft.
Garage — 976 sq. ft.

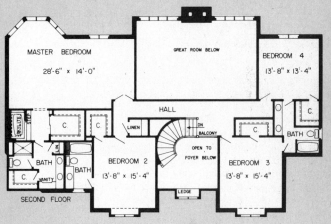

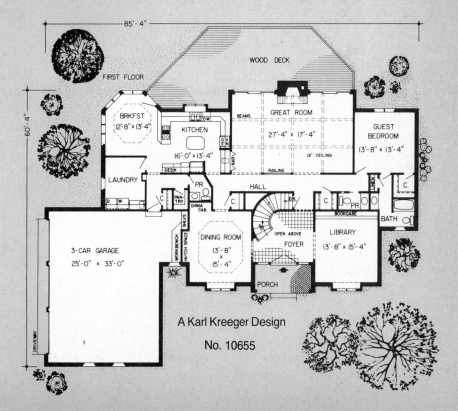

A Karl Kreeger Design

No. 10655

Three Fireplaces Provide Warm Feeling

No. 10670

Vaulted ceilings, a gently curving staircase, and high, arched windows make the entry to this spacious, five-bedroom home an airy celebration of light and space. A short hall leads from the formal dining room to the cozy family room, island kitchen, and sunny breakfast nook with adjoining brick patio. Warmed by its own fireplace, the master bedroom shares a private wing on the first floor with a bedroom that could double as a study. The second floor deck off the library is a great place to enjoy a sunny afternoon. And, don't worry about storage. Two pantries, a room-sized wet bar, and walk-in closets in every bedroom mean you'll never have to worry about clutter.

First floor — 2,959 sq. ft.
Second floor — 1,076 sq. ft.
Garage — 764 sq. ft.

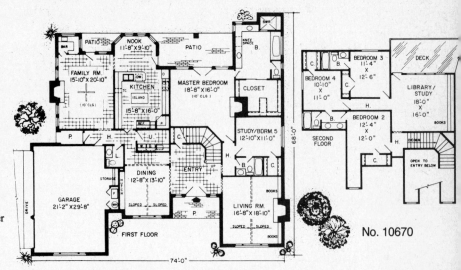

No. 10670

Contemporary Features Distinct Angles

No. 10554

A personable dining room connects to a very large, conveniently planned kitchen. Off the kitchen is the breakfast room whose sliding glass doors lead to an outdoor brick patio. The master bedroom enjoys a private bath, walk-in closet, and an intimate view of the fenced private garden. Other options include an open beamed living room that is separated from the dining room by a partial wood railing. The second level has two bedrooms, one with a walk-in closet, which share a complete bath.

First floor — 1,816 sq. ft.
Second floor — 642 sq. ft.
Basement — 1,816 sq. ft.
Garage — 591 sq. ft.

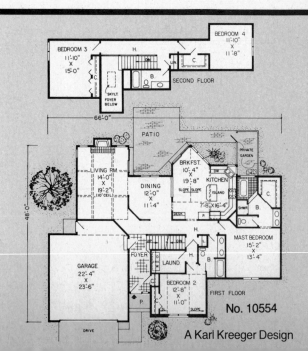

No. 10554

A Karl Kreeger Design

Three Bedroom Design Features Sloped Ceilings, Octagonal Rooms

No. 10505

The luxurious master suite of this uniquely designed, three bedroom home is secluded on an upper floor. It is linked to the stairway by a balcony which overlooks the first floor family room and central hall. Additionally it features a full wall of double closets, a sloped ceiling and a private fireplace. The octagonal, five-piece bath also features a sloped ceiling. The octagonal treatment is carried out in the first floor nook which adjoins the kitchen and in the arrangement of the casement windows in the living room. The family room boasts a corner fireplace and has its own sloped ceiling. Two additional bedrooms, each with a large closet, a four-piece bath, and a conveniently located laundry room complete this unusual and inviting home.

First floor — 1,704 sq. ft.
Second floor — 561 sq. ft.
Garage — 439 sq. ft.

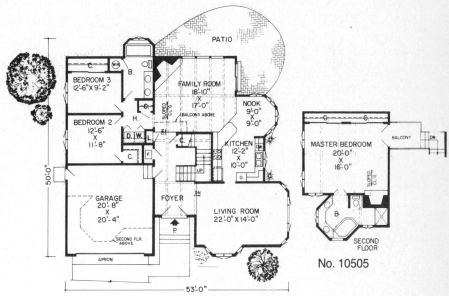

No. 10505

Vaulted Ceilings Create Impressive Entry

No. 9269

Vaulted ceilings and a profusion of windows set this A-frame design alive with height and drama. The imposing living room is rendered comfortable by its woodburning fireplace, and it adjoins the open kitchen and family room, separated by a breakfast bar. Two bedrooms with copious closet space, plus a full bath, complete the main level. The upper level houses another bedroom and bath, as well as an ample hobby room which might be furnished with a sofa bed to convert it to a guest room when necessary. A covered patio is reached through the family room.

First floor — 1,285 sq. ft.
Second floor — 476 sq. ft.
Garage — 473 sq. ft.

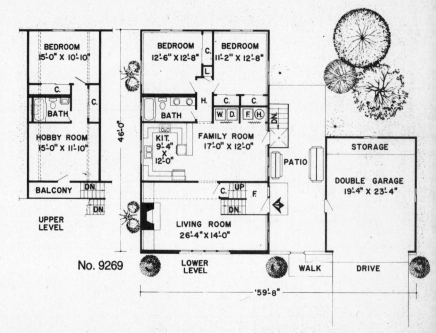

Impact Two-story Design Ideal for Small Lot

No. 10517

On the second floor of this well-arranged home are two bedrooms which flank a bath that is illuminated by a skylight. Adjacent to the bath are individual dressing areas each with its own basin and large walk-in closet. The interesting angles incorporated into the plan of the first floor create extra space in the master suite. The living room has a sloped ceiling and a fireplace with tile hearth. The angular kitchen includes a pantry, space for a dinette set and direct access to the rear deck. Other features include a half bath on the first floor, a conveniently located laundry, and an inviting two-story foyer.

First floor — 1,171 sq. ft.
Second floor — 561 sq. ft.
Basement — 1,171 sq. ft.
Garage — 484 sq. ft.

A Karl Kreeger Design

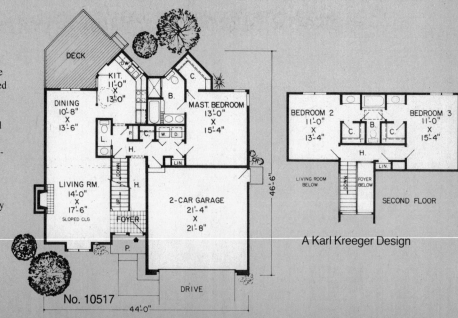

Studio Strengthens Dutch Colonial

No. 10016

Reminiscent of a Dutch Colonial farmhouse, this massive triple-sectioned design is heightened by a serviceable studio or game room above the garage. Emphasizing privacy, the design groups three bedrooms and two baths in a second floor sleeping wing and further separates the master bedroom by closets, bath, and stairway. Sliding glass doors open the family room and firelit living room to terraces. The dining room is set apart to stress formality. Bordering the kitchen is a combination laundry and half bath.

First floor — 1,256 sq. ft.
Second floor — 815 sq. ft.
Game room — 384 sq. ft.
Garage — 576 sq. ft.
Basement — 936 sq. ft.

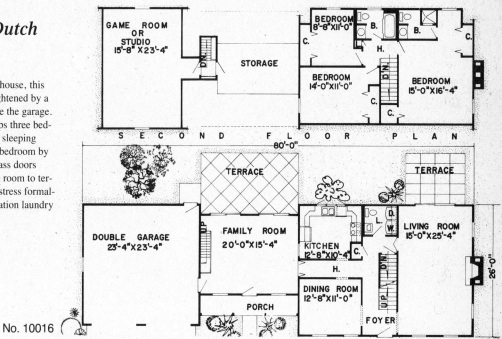

GAME ROOM OR STUDIO 15'-8" X 23'-4"

STORAGE

BEDROOM 8'-8" X 12'-0"

BEDROOM 14'-0" X 11'-0"

BEDROOM 15'-0" X 16'-4"

S E C O N D F L O O R P L A N

DOUBLE GARAGE 23'-4" X 23'-4"

TERRACE

FAMILY ROOM 20'-0" X 15'-4"

KITCHEN 12'-8" X 10'-4"

TERRACE

LIVING ROOM 15'-0" X 25'-4"

DINING ROOM 12'-8" X 11'-0"

PORCH

FOYER

80'-0"

26'-0"

No. 10016

Two-Story Window Flanked By Stone Dominates Facade

No. 10494

The tiled foyer leads conveniently leads to the upper two bedrooms, the master bedroom, and the central living room. A corner built-in bookcase, fireplace and dramatic window wall complete this gracious room. The front dining room, enhanced by natural lighting, is convenient to the kitchen and adjacent breakfast nook.

First floor — 1,584 sq. ft.
Second floor — 599 sq. ft.
Basement — 1,584 sq. ft.
Garage — 514 sq. ft.

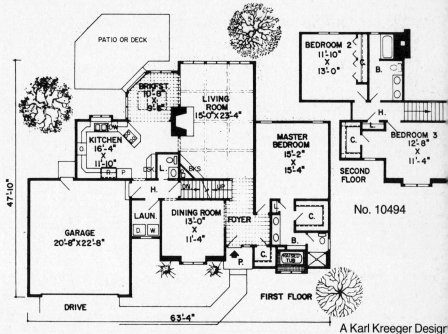

No. 10494

A Karl Kreeger Design

Passive Solar with Unique Great Room

No. 10380

Expanses of glass and rugged exposed beams dominate the front of this design's six-sided living center, creating a contemporary look that would be outstanding in any setting. Angled service and sleeping wings flow to the right and left, creating unusual shaped rooms and leaving nooks and crannies for storage. Spiral stairs just inside the tiled entry rise to a loft overlooking the great room. All rooms have sloped ceilings with R-38 insulation while sidewalls call for R-24. Living and dining possibilities are expanded by use of the rear patio and deck. A full basement lies under the house.

First floor — 2,199 sq. ft.
Loft — 336 sq. ft.
Garage — 611 sq. ft.
Basement — 2,199 sq. ft.

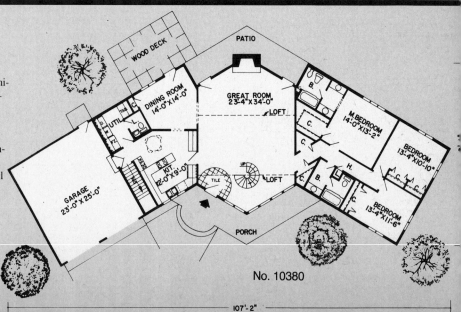

No. 10380

Balcony and Spiral Staircase Accent Traditional Four-bedroom

No. 10537

This roomy kitchen comes complete with a pantry and lots of cabinet space. The unique morning room is complemented with a large fireplace and an entry onto the patio for year 'round enjoyment. All four bedrooms are complete with full baths and walk-in closets.

First floor — 3,114 sq. ft.
Second floor — 924 sq. ft.
Basement — 3,092 sq. ft.
Garage — 917 sq. ft.

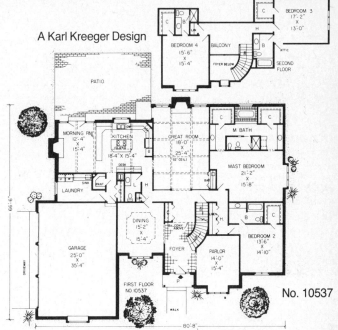

A Karl Kreeger Design

No. 10537

Bedroom Tower Creates Interesting Roof Line

No. 10618

Sloping ceilings and lofty open spaces are dominant features in this four-bedroom family home. Leading from the stairs to a full bath and two bedrooms, the upstairs hall is a bridge over the foyer and rustic living room. The dining room lies just off the foyer, adjacent to the island kitchen and breakfast room. The vaulted master suite with attached deck, a family bath, and bedroom with walk-in closet occupy a private wing.

First floor — 1,492 sq. ft.
Second floor — 475 sq. ft.
Garage — 413 sq. ft.

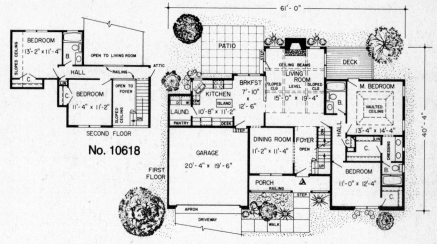

No. 10618

A Karl Kreeger Design

Sunlight at its Best

No. 26400

This energy efficient 2-story solar home is as attractive on the inside as it is inviting on the outside. This house is designed for ease of maintenance with redwood siding and battens. The rooftop solar collectors are shown on the southern side over the 2-story sunroom and the heat storage unit is directly beneath the floor of the sunroom. The upper level shows three spacious bedrooms with a centrally located expansive bath. The master bedroom features double closets and plenty of storage space. Sliding glass doors open from the master suite onto the balcony overlooking the sunroom. Another bedroom opens onto a private deck.

First floor — 1,037 sq. ft. (including sunroom)
Second floor — 770 sq. ft.
Basement — 748 sq. ft.
Garage — 422 sq. ft.

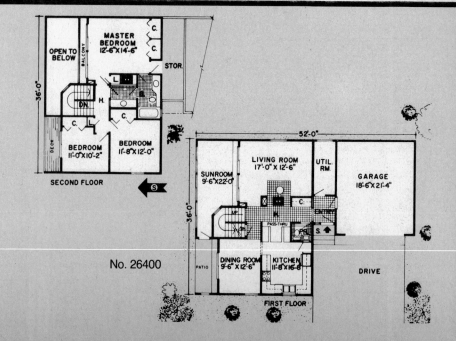

No. 26400

Sunny and Spacious

No. 20302

The wood detailing that radiates from the half round window of this inviting family home hints at the sunny atmosphere you'll find inside. Walking through the vestibule past the formal and family dining rooms, you'll encounter a two-way fireplace that warms the living and family rooms at the rear of the house. Notice the double sliders that link both rooms to a massive rear deck, and the pass-through convenience afforded by the U-shaped kitchen. Tucked behind the garage for privacy, the first-floor master suite features a skylit bath with double vanities and a luxurious spa tub. And, upstairs, three bedrooms open to a skylit lounge with a bird's eye view of the family room.

First floor — 1,510 sq. ft.
Second floor — 820 sq. ft.
Basement — 1,284 sq. ft.
Garage — 430 sq. ft.

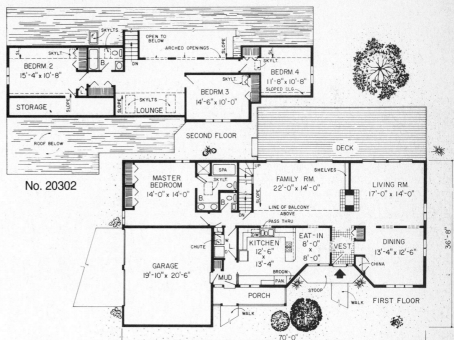

No. 20302

SOLAR HOME

Arches Grace Classic Facade

No. 10677

Do you have a small lot, but love open space? Here's your answer! This compact beauty uses built-in planters and half-walls to define rooms without closing them in. Look at the first floor plan. The living room features a cozy sitting area dominated by a half-round window, then rises to nearly two stories for a wide-open feeling. At the rear of the house, the family room and kitchen, divided only by a cooktop peninsula, share the airy atmosphere. Sliders unite this sunny area with an outdoor patio that mirrors the shape of the dining bay. Peer down at the living room from your vantage point on the balcony that connects the three bedrooms upstairs. And, be sure to notice the double sinks and built-in vanity in the master bath, a plus when you're rushed in the morning.

First floor — 932 sq. ft.
Second floor — 764 sq. ft.
Garage — 430 sq. ft.
Basement — 920 sq. ft.

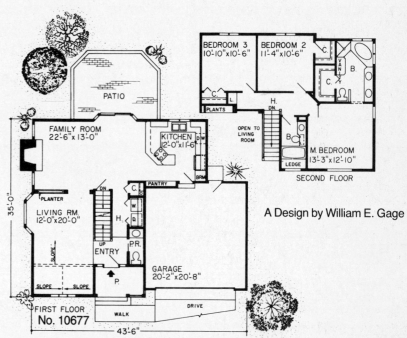

A Design by William E. Gage

Two Story Master Bedroom Featured

No. 19701

With both master bedroom and living room extending two stories, this contemporary home achieves a dramatic interior. Sliding glass doors open both rooms to the terrace, and a family room and separate dining room are shown. A total of four bedrooms, some with built-in desks or bookshelves, adequately provide sleeping space.

First floor — 1,511 sq. ft.
Second floor — 495 sq. ft.
Garage — 420 sq. ft.

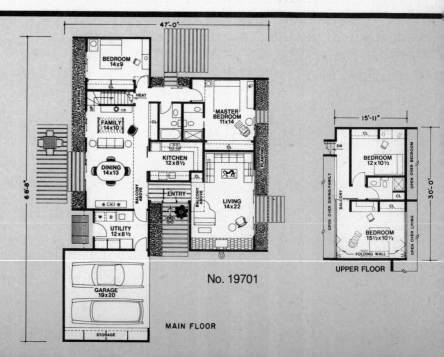

No. 19701

Vaulted Ceilings Make Every Room Special

No. 10698

This gracious five-bedroom family home offers spectacular views, both inside and out. Survey the two-story morning room and yard beyond from a vantage point upstairs. Two bedrooms adjoining a full bath and covered deck share the upper level with the loft. Enjoy the same view from the island kitchen, separated from the morning room only by a counter. Delight in pool vistas from a covered patio, or from living and family rooms. Both have beamed, ten-foot ceilings, massive fireplaces, and share a wetbar and access to the patio. Gaze at the stars through the skylight over the bath in the master suite. Down a hallway behind double doors, the suite features a raised tub, built-in dressing tables, and fireplaced sitting room with vaulted ceiling.

First floor — 4,014 sq. ft.
Second floor — 727 sq. ft.
Garage — 657 sq. ft.

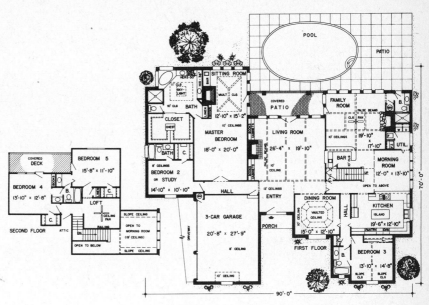

No. 10698

Designed for Entertaining

No. 10587

The double doors of the vaulted entry are just a hint of the graceful touches in this three-bedroom home. Curves soften the stairway, deck, and the huge bar that runs between the formal and informal dining areas. Skylights, bay, and bump-out windows flood every room with light. And when the sun goes down, you can keep things cozy with fireplaces in the family and sunken living rooms. For a quiet retreat, sneak upstairs to deck off the master bedroom suite.

First floor — 2,036 sq. ft.
Second floor — 1,554 sq. ft.
Garage — 533 sq. ft.

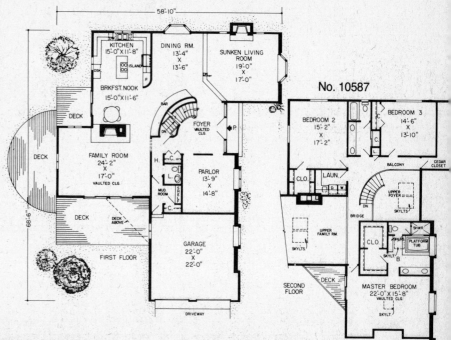

Four Bedrooms Have Luxury Master Suite Plus Guest Room

No. 10510

Three of this home's four bedrooms are located on the second floor with the fourth on the first floor with its own private bath. It's an ideal arrangement for the multi-generation family. The second floor master suite is large and luxurious with a private deck, double vanity in the dressing area that includes a walk-in closet, plus a master bath which has both a shower and a round tub. Two more bedrooms and a bath complete the upper story. The large, first floor family room has a fully appointed bar area, a fireplace, and access to the patio. The breakfast nook overlooks the family room and adjoins the efficiently-designed kitchen. There's also a formal dining room, a sunken living room and a three-car garage.

First floor — 1,485 sq. ft.
Second floor — 958 sq. ft.
Garage — 723 sq. ft.

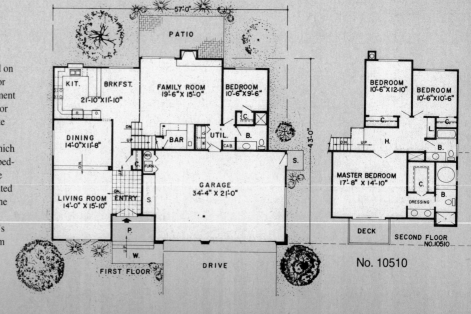

Angular Design is Strikingly Contemporary

No. 10469

The living room is the focal point of this contemporary design and incorporates several innovative features. Its vaulted ceiling is highlighted with exposed beams, and the angled front has up to four levels of windows which are operated by remote control. A wood-burning fireplace and built-in bookshelves enhance the rear wall of the room. The kitchen, informal serving area and dining room occupy the remainder of the first floor. The second floor is reserved for the three spacious bedrooms. The master bedroom also has a beamed ceiling plus its own fireplace.

First floor — 989 sq. ft.
Second floor — 810 sq. ft.
Garage — 538 sq. ft.

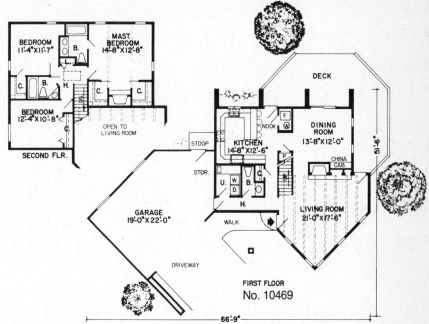

SECOND FLR.

BEDROOM 11'-4"X11'-7"

MAST. BEDROOM 14'-8"X12'-8"

BEDROOM 12'-4"X10'-8"

OPEN TO LIVING ROOM

DECK

KITCHEN 14'-8"X12'-6"

NOOK

DINING ROOM 13'-8"X12'-0"

CHINA CAB.

STOOP

STOR.

GARAGE 19'-0"X22'-0"

WALK

LIVING ROOM 21'-0"X17'-6"

51'-6"

DRIVEWAY

FIRST FLOOR
No. 10469

66'-9"

Classic Warmth

No. 10684

This compact traditional with clapboard exterior and inviting, sheltered entry boasts loads of features that make it a special home. Look at the built-in seat by the garage entry, the handy breakfast bar that separates the kitchen and family room, and the convenient powder room just off the foyer. Cathedral ceilings lend an airy quality to the living and dining rooms. A single step down keeps the two rooms separate without compromising the open feeling that's so enjoyable. Sliders lead from both dining and family rooms to the rear patio, making it an excellent location for an outdoor party. Tucked upstairs, the three bedrooms include your own, private master suite.

First floor — 940 sq. ft.
Second floor — 720 sq. ft.
Walkout basement — 554 sq. ft.
Garage — 418 sq. ft.
Crawl space — 312 sq. ft.

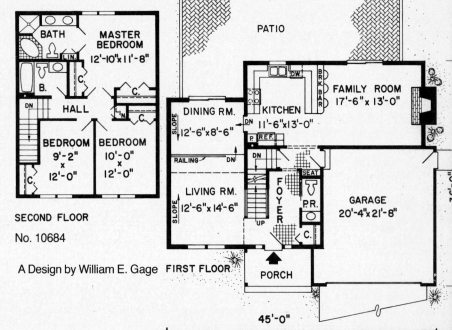

A Design by William E. Gage

Easy-Living Plan

No. 10574

Don't worry about storage problems in this sprawling traditional. Every inch of space is put to good use. The well designed floor plan revolves around a two-story central foyer. You'll find utility and dining areas grouped together. The screened porch off the breakfast room is a lovely mealtime spot on a summer day. Right down the hall, family and living rooms insure a cozy atmosphere day and night with expansive windows and fireplaces. You'll find the master suite, with its double vanities and room-size closet, tucked away at the end of the hall. The kids won't have much trouble keeping their rooms clean with extra-large closets, window seat storage, and their own bath upstairs.

First floor — 2,215 sq. ft.
Second floor — 1,025 sq. ft.
Basement — 2,215 sq. ft.
Garage and storage — 618 sq. ft.

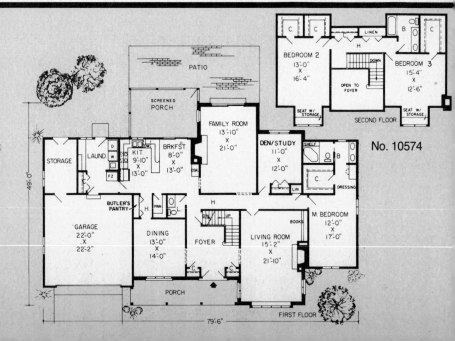

No. 10574

Contemporary Design Features Four Bedrooms and Three-car Garage

No. 10488

An ideal home for a family with teenagers, this striking design is enhanced by the interesting window treatment in both the kitchen and dining rooms. The first floor includes formal living and dining rooms as well as a large family room complete with a fireplace and a wetbar. The first floor bedroom with its private entrance to the bath would be ideal for guests. Highlighting the second floor is the spacious master bedroom which adjoins a luxurious dressing room with an extra large walk-in closet. Two more bedrooms flank an additional bath. The second floor balcony yields a commanding view of the first floor living and dining rooms.

First floor — 1,540 sq. ft.
Second floor — 1,122 sq. ft.
Garage — 626 sq. ft.

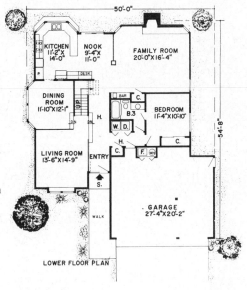

LOWER FLOOR PLAN

No. 10488

UPPER FLOOR PLAN

Compact Charmer Flooded with Sun

No. 20300

The clerestory window high over the covered porch of this inviting gem hints at the high excitement you'll find when you walk through the front door. From the soaring foyer to the sun room off the fire-placed living room and kitchen, this contemporary porch revival house is enveloped in warmth and sunlight. And, you'll find all the features you've been longing for: built in media and china cabinets, an efficient U-shaped kitchen, a central yet concealed first-floor powder room, a skylit master bath with double vanities, and three spacious bedrooms with loads of closet space.

First floor — 909 sq. ft.
Second floor — 765 sq. ft.
Basement — 517 sq. ft.
Garage and stair — 479 sq. ft.

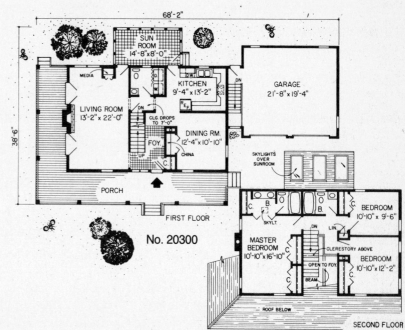

Room to Expand

No. 10525

In addition to the three, well-designed bedrooms, the second floor of this traditional design features a large unfinished area which could be a study, hobby center or even a fully-equipped exercise room. The luxury master suite has two walk-in closets in the dressing area plus a conveniently arranged five-piece bath which features a circular window above the tiled tub enclosure. The first floor is composed of formal dining and living rooms on either side of the tiled foyer with the family areas organized along the back overlooking the patio. The cozy family room has a fireplace, built-in bookcase and opens onto the patio. The kitchen features a bump-out window over the sink and shares a snack bar with the bright and cheery breakfast nook.

First floor — 1,219 sq. ft.
Second floor — 1,010 sq. ft.
Basement — 1,219 sq. ft.
Garage — 514 sq. ft.

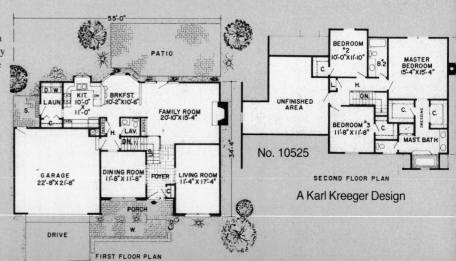

A Karl Kreeger Design

28

Contemporary Castle

No. 10697

With glass walls in every room, this gracious home deserves a beautiful setting. Whether you're swimming, entertaining, or just want to relax, you'll find a perfect spot — patios and a deck surround living spaces upstairs and down. And, this house isn't just beautiful. Convenient features abound throughout. Notice how eating areas flank the roomy island kitchen and utility areas, and how the family and living rooms share a wetbar and back-to-back fireplaces. Every bedroom adjoins a bath, but the master suite, with its recessed ceilings, private sitting room with a walled patio, and double walk-in closets is a luxurious retreat that's hard to resist.

First floor — 2,740 sq. ft.
Second floor — 948 sq. ft.
Garage — 522 sq. ft.

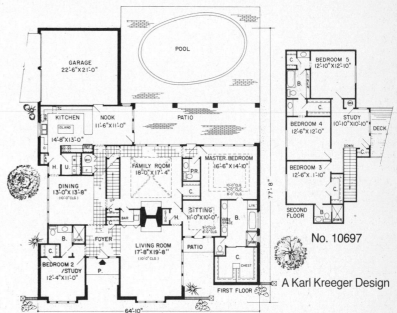

No. 10697

A Karl Kreeger Design

You Deserve this Classic Beauty

No. 20094

Sturdy stucco, fieldstone, and rough-hewn timbers lend a distinguished air to this updated Tudor classic. And inside, modern and traditional elements unite to create a masterpiece your family will never outgrow. Look at the soaring foyer, the elegant recessed ceilings in the dining room and master suite, and the book-lined library off the fireplaced living room. Imagine the convenience of an island kitchen with wetbar service to the living room, and an adjoining, skylit breakfast room. And, think about how the three-and-a-half baths that serve the first-floor master suite and three upstairs bedrooms will make the morning rush a thing of the past.

First floor — 2,047 sq. ft.
Second floor — 789 sq. ft.
Basement — 2,047 sq. ft.
Garage — 524 sq. ft.

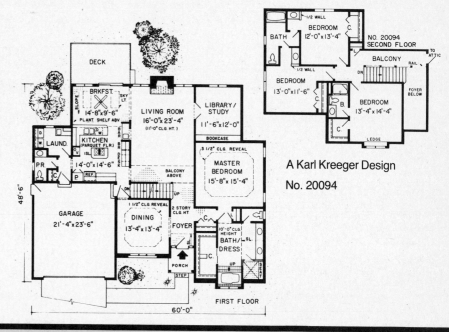

A Karl Kreeger Design
No. 20094

Facade Features Vertical Columns

No. 10645

This two story home is perfect for the family that wants to keep sleeping quarters quiet. Closets and a hallway muffle sound from the foyer. Upstairs, the location of two additional bedrooms and full skylit bath over the garage and sleeping areas below insures a restful atmosphere. The dining room is located directly off the foyer. With an angular ceiling and massive fireplace, the great room opens to the kitchen and breakfast nook, which features sliding glass doors to an outdoor patio.

First floor — 1,628 sq. ft.
Second floor — 609 sq. ft.
Basement — 1,616 sq. ft.
Garage — 450 sq. ft.

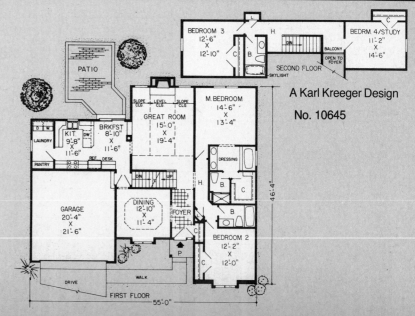

A Karl Kreeger Design
No. 10645

Stylish and Practical Plan

No. 20069

Make the most of daily life with a stylish and practical plan. The garage and seldom-used formal dining room separate the main areas of the house from traffic noise, while the rear of the home maximizes comfort and livability. The kitchen contains a breakfast area large enough for most informal meals and serves snacks to the living room or deck equally well. The spacious living room is a joy in either summer or winter thanks to the fireplace and broad views of deck and back yard. All bedrooms have plenty of closet space, and you'll especialy appreciate the attic storage.

First floor — 1,313 sq. ft.
Second floor — 588 sq. ft.
Basement — 1,299 sq. ft.

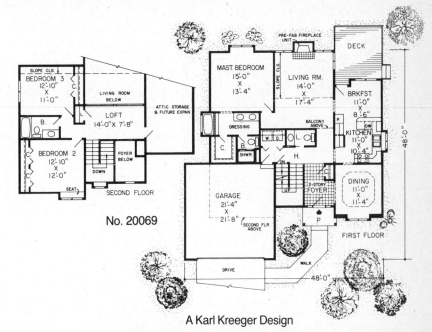

No. 20069

A Karl Kreeger Design

Contemporary Floor Plan Blends with Distinctive Exterior

No. 10500

Lots of living is packed into this well organized design. The expansive Great Room is accented by a massive fireplace and a beamed, cathedral ceiling. The kitchen and breakfast area includes a charming and efficient angled cooking center, while the formal dining room is convenient yet protected from noise. Indulge yourself in the master suite with its luxurious 5-piece bath, including a raised tile tub. Three bedrooms and a loft, which opens onto the foyer, are located on the second floor. Each bedroom has a walk-in closet and direct access to a full bath.

First floor — 2,188 sq. ft.
Second floor — 1,083 sq. ft.
Basement — 2,188 sq. ft.
Garage — 576 sq. ft.

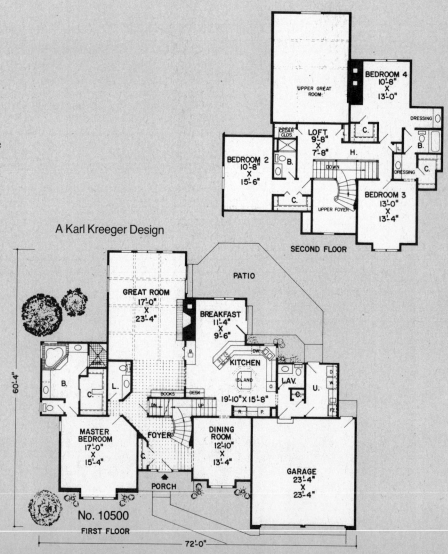

A Karl Kreeger Design

SECOND FLOOR

No. 10500
FIRST FLOOR

Compact Home is Surprisingly Spacious

No. 90905

Searching for a design where the living room takes advantage of both front and rear views? Look no further. And, this cozy ranch has loads of other features. An attractive porch welcomes guests and provides shade for the big living room window on hot summer days. A large covered sundeck adjacent to the living room, dining room and kitchen will make entertaining a delight. The roomy bedrooms, including the master suite with full bath and a walk-in closet, are protected from street noise by the two-car garage.

Main floor — 1,314 sq. ft.
Basement — 1,488 sq. ft.
Garage — 484 sq. ft.
Width — 50 ft.
Depth — 54 ft.

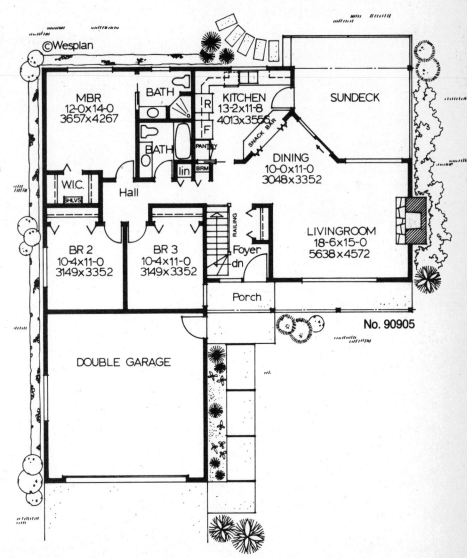

©Wesplan

MBR
12-0x14-0
3657x4267

BATH

KITCHEN
13-2x11-8
4013x3556

SUNDECK

BATH

PANTRY

DINING
10-0x11-0
3048x3352

lin

BRM

W.I.C.

SHLVS

Hall

LIVINGROOM
18-6x15-0
5638x4572

BR 2
10-4x11-0
3149x3352

BR 3
10-4x11-0
3149x3352

RAILING

Foyer
dn

Porch

No. 90905

DOUBLE GARAGE

A Home for Your Growing Family

No. 10692

Walk into this gracious family home and you can see it's designed for convenient living. Formal living and dining rooms flank the two-story entry. Look up to discover the sunny study that links the four upstairs bedrooms and adjoining baths.

From the central hallway with handy powder room, you can reach the master suite or the family living suite that features a roomy, angular kitchen, utility room, breakfast nook, and fireplaced family room.

First floor — 2,313 sq. ft.
Second floor — 1,256 sq. ft.
Garage — 662 sq. ft.

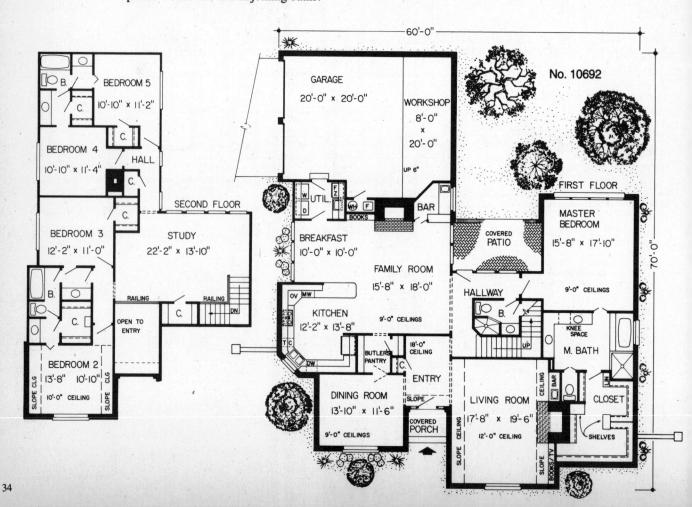

Natural Lighting Built into Design

No. 10547

Clever use of skylights in the foyer and master bedroom's bath area add creative natural lighting to this home. The sun room is a passive solar feature which, if turned south, will help heat the house.

Unique in design, this ranch incorporates many options. Its large kitchen and breakfast area with an adjoining laundry offers convenience as a priority. The open dining and living areas display a profound sense of expansiveness, while a more formal dining area may be added by partitioning off the area. The master bedroom with its adjoining bath offers

both a tub and a shower plus a walk-in closet.

First floor — 1,607 sq. ft.
Second floor — 623 sq. ft.
Basement — 1,542 sq. ft.
Garage — 484 sq. ft.

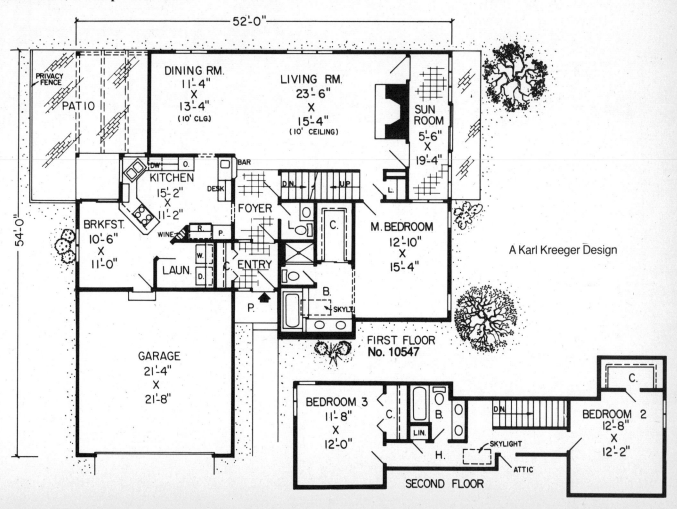

A Karl Kreeger Design

Rear Deck Adds Outdoor Living Space

No. 10746

This three-bedroom beauty boasts an updated wood and brick exterior, oversized windows, and a sheltered entry you'll appreciate on a rainy day. If you do get caught in a downpour, step down the entry hall past the formal dining room to the two-story great room, and dry off by the fire. The handy kitchen, just across the counter from a cozy breakfast nook, features a built-in pantry and planning desk, just steps away from the garage entry. And, the first-floor master suite with its own private bath is an added convenience you're sure to enjoy. Two upstairs bedrooms share a full bath and a balcony vantage of the great room below.

First floor — 1,753 sq. ft.
Second floor — 549 sq. ft.
Garage — 513 sq. ft.

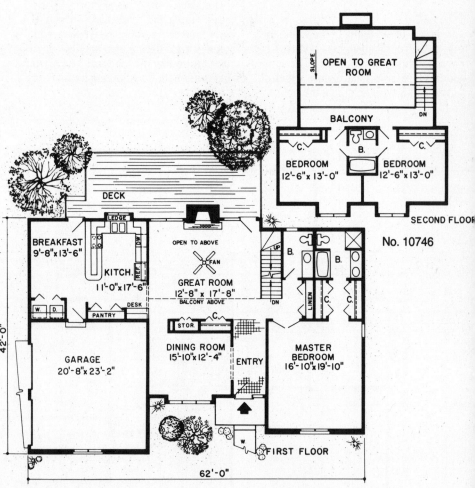

Excellent Choice for Sloping Lot

No. 9714

With its sloping, striking design, this split foyer plan combines outdoor living areas and a highly livable lower level. Facing the front and opening to terrace, the family room dominates the lower level, which also includes a bedroom, a hobby room, and a full bath with shower. Above, a sun deck greets the living room and dining room. A tiled country kitchen, complete with a cooking island and built-in laundry, and three bedrooms and two full baths comprise the sleeping wing.

Main level — 1,748 sq. ft.
Lower level — 932 sq. ft.
Garage — 768 sq. ft.

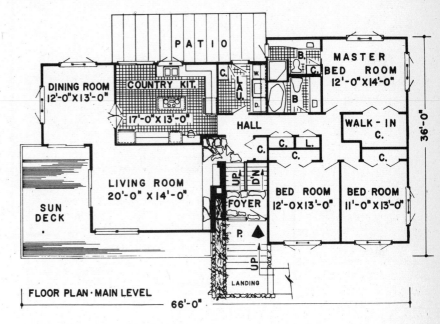

FLOOR PLAN · MAIN LEVEL

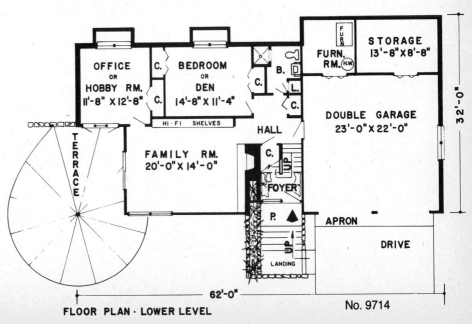

FLOOR PLAN · LOWER LEVEL

No. 9714

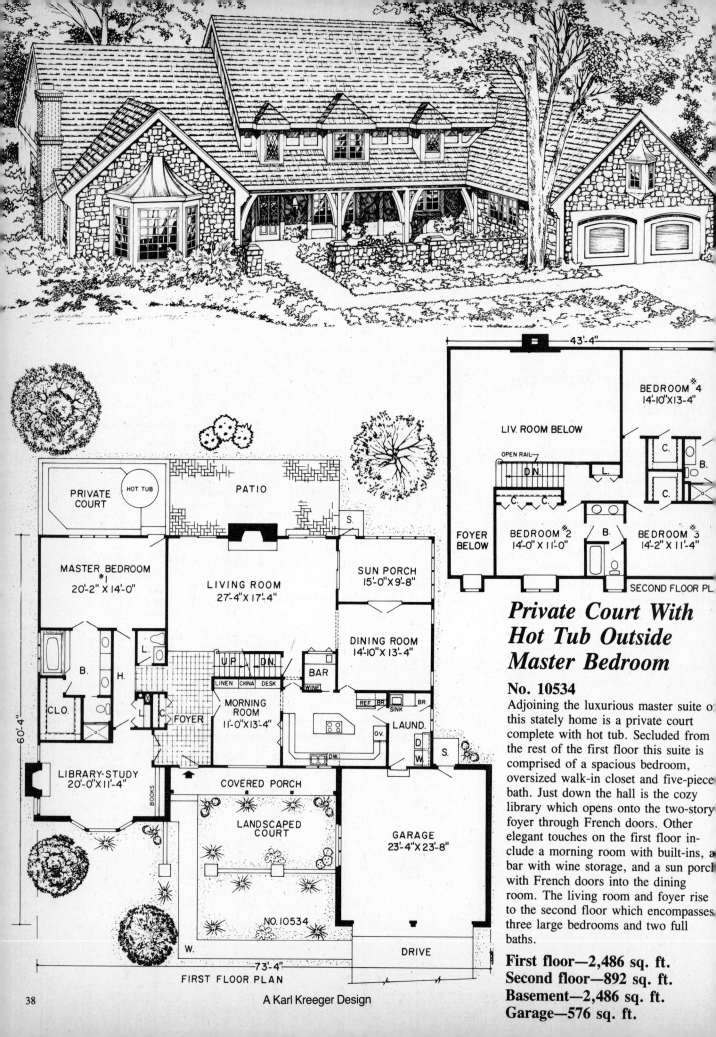

Private Court With Hot Tub Outside Master Bedroom

No. 10534

Adjoining the luxurious master suite of this stately home is a private court complete with hot tub. Secluded from the rest of the first floor this suite is comprised of a spacious bedroom, oversized walk-in closet and five-piece bath. Just down the hall is the cozy library which opens onto the two-story foyer through French doors. Other elegant touches on the first floor include a morning room with built-ins, a bar with wine storage, and a sun porch with French doors into the dining room. The living room and foyer rise to the second floor which encompasses three large bedrooms and two full baths.

First floor—2,486 sq. ft.
Second floor—892 sq. ft.
Basement—2,486 sq. ft.
Garage—576 sq. ft.

PRIVATE COURT

HOT TUB

PATtO

MASTER BEDROOM #1
20'-2" X 14'-0"

LIVING ROOM
27'-4" X 17'-4"

SUN PORCH
15'-0" X 9'-8"

DINING ROOM
14'-10" X 13'-4"

B.

H.

CLO.

UP   DN.

LINEN   CHINA   DESK

BAR

WINE

MORNING ROOM
11'-0" X 13'-4"

FOYER

REF BR.

SINK BR.

LAUND.

OV.

D. S.
W.

LIBRARY-STUDY
20'-0" X 11'-4"

BOOKS

DW

COVERED PORCH

LANDSCAPED COURT

GARAGE
23'-4" X 23'-8"

NO. 10534

60'-4"

W.

73'-4"

DRIVE

FIRST FLOOR PLAN

43'-4"

BEDROOM #4
14'-10" X 13'-4"

LIV. ROOM BELOW

OPEN RAIL

DN.

C. C.

L.

C.

B.

FOYER BELOW

BEDROOM #2
14'-0" X 11'-0"

B.

BEDROOM #3
14'-2" X 11'-4"

SECOND FLOOR PL.

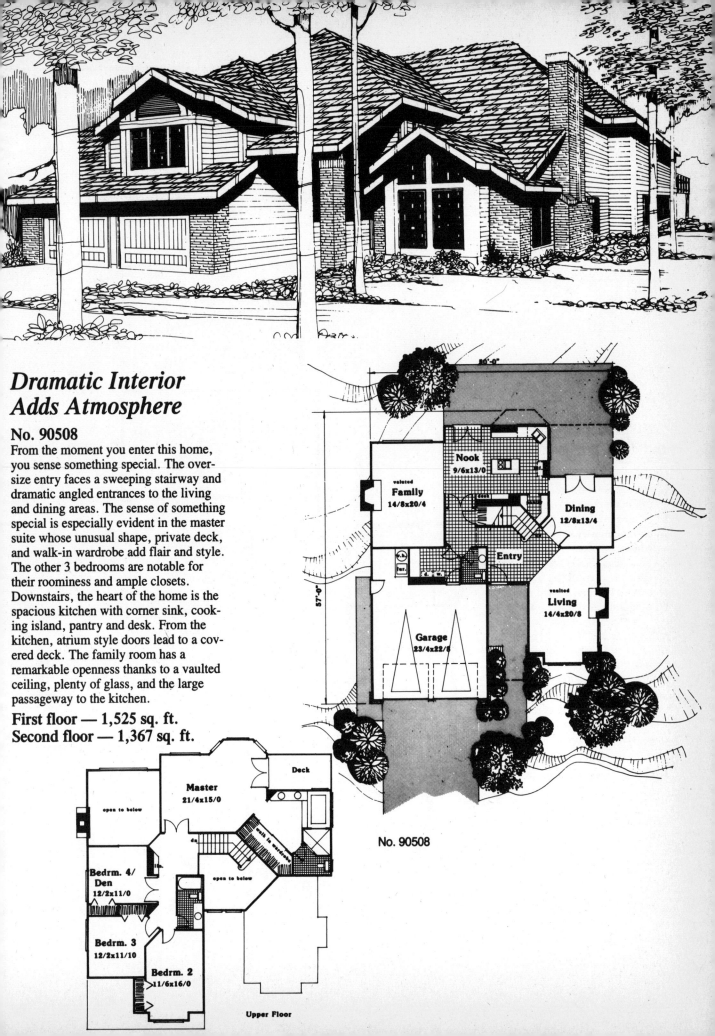

Dramatic Interior
Adds Atmosphere

No. 90508

From the moment you enter this home, you sense something special. The over-size entry faces a sweeping stairway and dramatic angled entrances to the living and dining areas. The sense of something special is especially evident in the master suite whose unusual shape, private deck, and walk-in wardrobe add flair and style. The other 3 bedrooms are notable for their roominess and ample closets. Downstairs, the heart of the home is the spacious kitchen with corner sink, cooking island, pantry and desk. From the kitchen, atrium style doors lead to a covered deck. The family room has a remarkable openness thanks to a vaulted ceiling, plenty of glass, and the large passageway to the kitchen.

First floor — 1,525 sq. ft.
Second floor — 1,367 sq. ft.

No. 90508

Upper Floor

Storage Space Plentiful

No. 10428

Practical division of living area locates the master suite at a distance from other living areas on the first floor. Only one small window is found in the suite's bathroom, but a large skylight above keeps the area well lit by natural light. In addition to the master suite, there are two more bedrooms upstairs which share a bath. The kitchen holds the central position in the remainder of the floor plan. Cabinet space is plentiful and a pantry provides additional storage space. A formal dining room, family room, and casual eating nook are nearby. The nook is completely open to the family room, adjoins the kitchen via a cabinet topped stub wall and enjoys outdoor expanses through stretches of glass on two walls, generating a roomy feeling for a smaller sized room. The living and family rooms and entry also sport generous use of glass.

First floor — 2,180 sq. ft.
Second floor — 646 sq. ft.
Covered patio — 368 sq. ft.
Garage — 470 sq. ft.

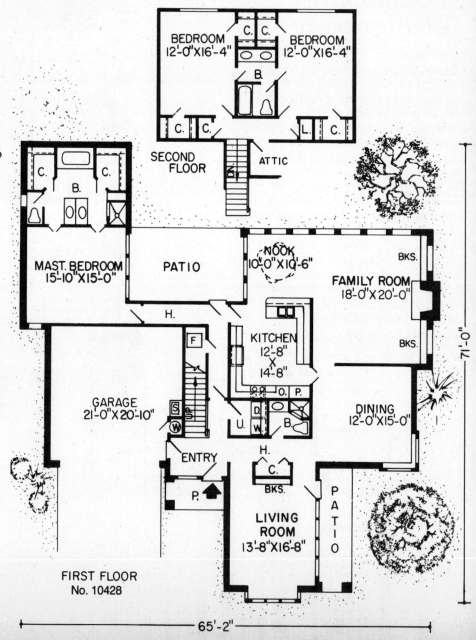

Loft Overlooks Attractive Foyer

No. 10583

This hillside home, characterized by enormous rooms and two garages, is built on two levels. From the foyer, travel down one hall to a cozy bedroom, full bath, island kitchen, laundry and garage. Or, walk straight into the sun-filled great and dining rooms with wrap-around deck. One room features a massive fireplace, built-in bookshelves, and access to the lofty study; the other contains a window greenhouse. For ultimate privacy, the master bedroom suite possesses a lavish skylit tub. On the lower level are two additional bedrooms, a bath, and a rec room with bar that opens onto an outdoor patio.

First floor — 2,367 sq. ft.
Basement (unfinished) — 372 sq. ft.
Basement (finished) — 1,241 sq. ft.
Loft — 295 sq. ft.
Garage (lower level) — 660 sq. ft.
Garage (upper level) — 636 sq. ft.

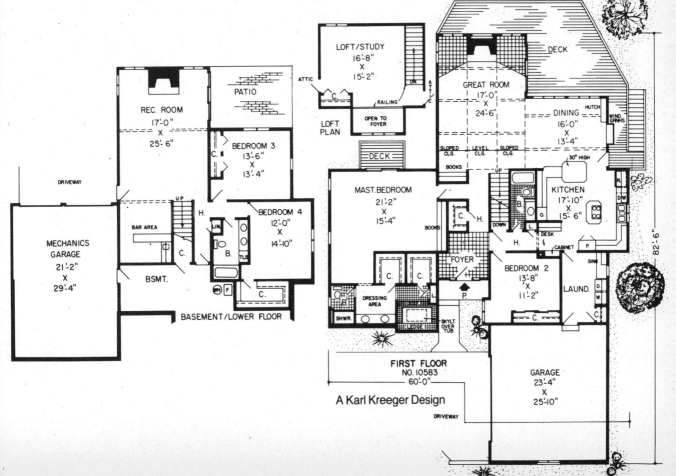

A Karl Kreeger Design

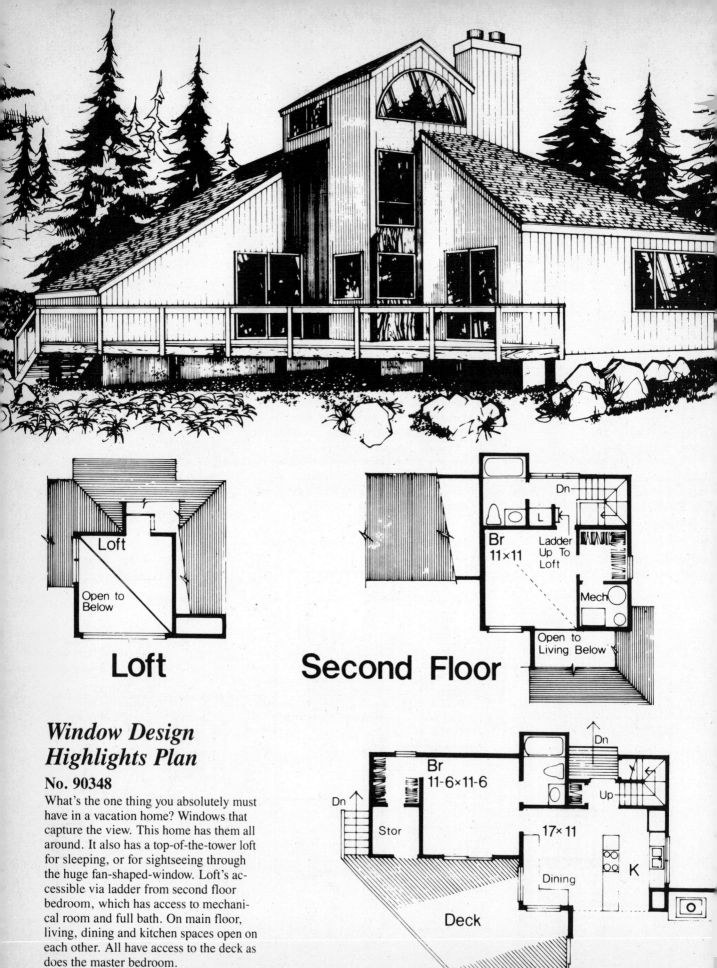

Loft

Second Floor

Window Design Highlights Plan

No. 90348

What's the one thing you absolutely must have in a vacation home? Windows that capture the view. This home has them all around. It also has a top-of-the-tower loft for sleeping, or for sightseeing through the huge fan-shaped-window. Loft's accessible via ladder from second floor bedroom, which has access to mechanical room and full bath. On main floor, living, dining and kitchen spaces open on each other. All have access to the deck as does the master bedroom.

Area — 1,097 sq. ft.

First Floor

Entertaining is No Problem

No. 10610

Start picking out the porch furniture. You won't be able to resist sitting on this magnificent veranda on a lazy summer day. Walking through the front door, you'll encounter a large planter that divides the entry from active areas at the rear of the house. You'll find a sunny bay with built-in seating in the formal dining room, which shares a massive, two-way fireplace with the vaulted, sunken living room. If the living room bar doesn't fill all your entertaining needs, the nearby island kitchen certainly will. And, if the crowd gets too large, the full-length deck, accessible from the living room or breakfast room, can handle the overflow. There are two bedrooms and a full bath on the first floor, but the master suite enjoys a private location at the top of the stairs.

First floor — 1,818 sq. ft.
Second floor — 528 sq. ft.
Basement — 1,818 sq. ft.

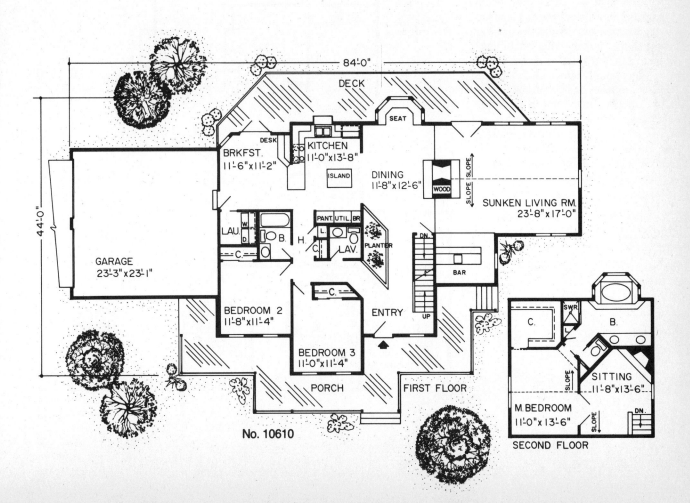

No. 10610

A Library in Every Room

No. 10686

Spectacular is one word you could use to describe the remarkable quality of light and space in this four-bedroom family home. Well-placed skylights and abundant windows bathe every room in sunlight. The huge, two-story foyer features an angular, open staircase that leads to the bedrooms, and divides the space between the vaulted living and dining rooms. At the rear of the house, the wide-open family area includes the kitchen, dinette, and fireplaced family room complete with built-in bar and bookcases. Vaulted ceilings in the screened porch are mirrored upstairs in the master suite, which features two walk-in closets, double vanities, and a luxurious jacuzzi.

First floor — 1,786 sq. ft.
Second floor — 1,490 sq. ft.
Basement — 1,773 sq. ft.
Garage — 579 sq. ft.

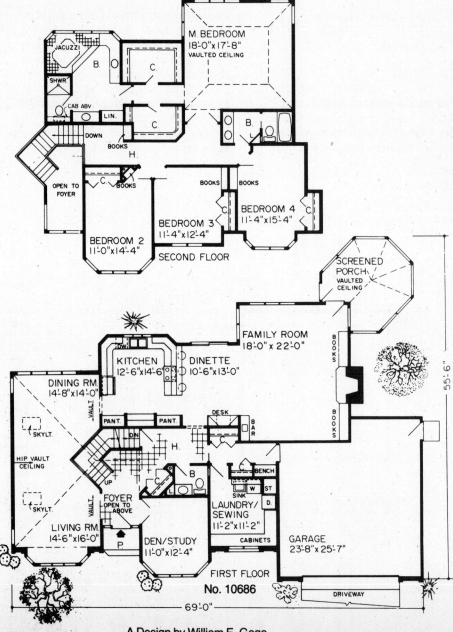

A Design by William E. Gage

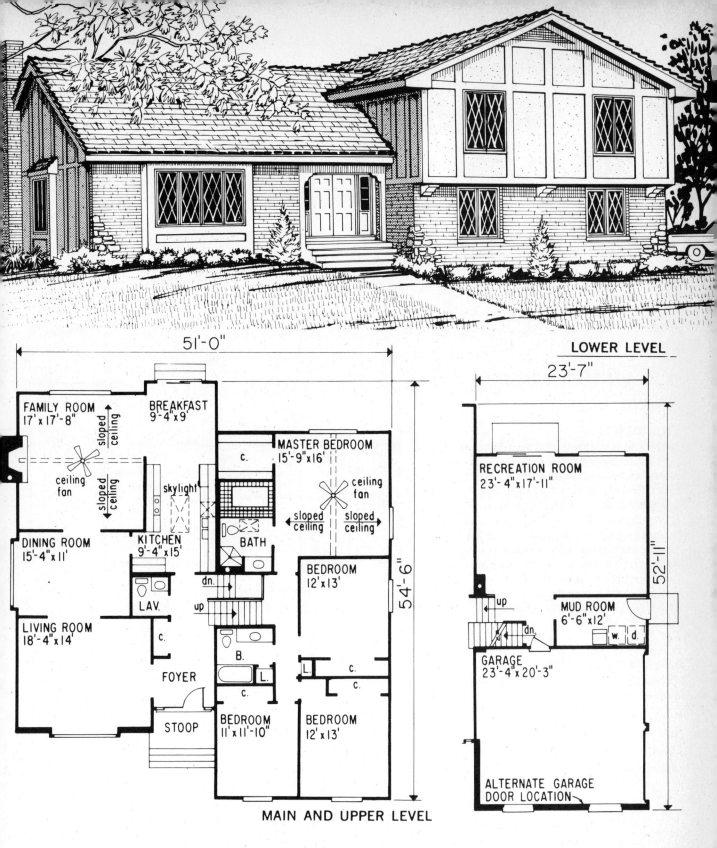

LOWER LEVEL

23'-7"

RECREATION ROOM
23'-4" x 17'-11"

52'-11"

MUD ROOM
6'-6" x 12"   w. d.

up

dn.

GARAGE
23'-4" x 20'-3"

ALTERNATE GARAGE
DOOR LOCATION

51'-0"

FAMILY ROOM
17' x 17'-8"   sloped ceiling   BREAKFAST
9'-4" x 9'

ceiling fan   sloped ceiling

MASTER BEDROOM
15'-9" x 16'

c.

skylight   ceiling fan

DINING ROOM
15'-4" x 11'   KITCHEN
9'-4" x 15'   BATH   sloped ceiling   sloped ceiling

LAV.   dn.   BEDROOM
12' x 13'

LIVING ROOM
18'-4" x 14'   c.   up

B.   L.   L.   c.

FOYER   c.   c.

STOOP   BEDROOM
11' x 11'-10"   BEDROOM
12' x 13'

54'-6"

MAIN AND UPPER LEVEL

English Tudor With Three Levels Plus Basement

No. 90160

The delightful tudor exterior is enhanced by the massive support posts and beam at the recessed entrance. Box bays and diamond lite windows add to the exterior charm. Flow from room to room in this well laid-out plan. The large living and dining rooms each have box bay windows. The family room features cathedral ceilings, and the spacious kitchen has a skylight and breakfast area with sloped ceiling and

patio doors. The upper level features four bedrooms, including the master suite with deluxe bath and walk-in closet. A two-car garage, mud room and oversized recreation room on the lower level help make this a home the entire family will enjoy.

Main & upper level—2,320 sq. ft. Lower level—600 sq. ft.

Rough Hewn Beams
Add Charm

No. 10611

With a screened porch and large patio off the family and breakfast rooms, you'll have lots of extra living space in warmer weather. Entertaining is a breeze with fireplaced family and living rooms and formal dining room. And when you want to get away from it all, retreat to the den across the hall from the laundry and powder room. Up the central staircase, you'll find 4 bedrooms and two full baths, including the master bedroom suite with walk in closet and dressing room.

First floor — 1,755 sq. ft.
Second floor — 1,334 sq. ft.
Basement — 1,755 sq. ft.
Garage — 692 sq. ft.

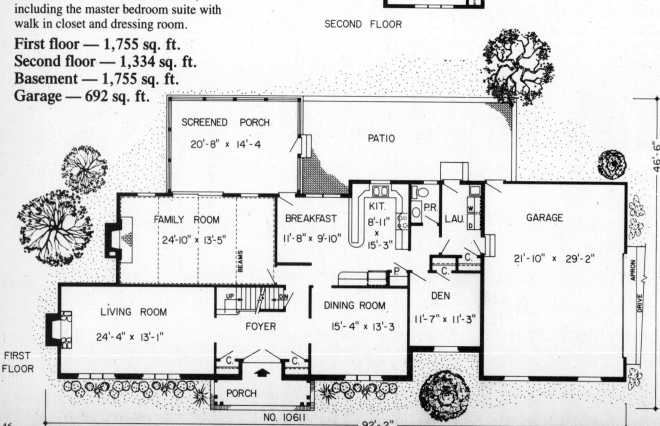

SECOND FLOOR

C.

VANITY

DRESSING   BATH   B.   C.

BEDROOM 4
13'-2" x 13'-3"

MASTER
BEDROOM
15'-3" x 17'-1"

HALL

ATTIC

STOR.   DN

BEDROOM 3
13'-2" x 13'-3"

BEDROOM 2
12'-4" x 13'-9"

C.

C.

SCREENED PORCH
20'-8" x 14'-4

PATIO

46'-6"

FAMILY ROOM
24'-10" x 13'-5"

BREAKFAST
11'-8" x 9'-10"

KIT.
8'-11"
x
15'-3"

P.R.

LAU.

W
D

GARAGE
21'-10" x 29'-2"

APRON

DRIVE

BEAMS

LIVING ROOM
24'-4" x 13'-1"

UP   DN

FOYER

DINING ROOM
15'-4" x 13'-3

P.

C.

DEN
11'-7" x 11'-3"

FIRST
FLOOR

C.   C.

PORCH

NO. 10611

92'-2"

Traditional Elements Combine in Friendly Colonial

No. 90606

Casual living is the theme of this elegant Farmhouse Colonial. A beautiful circular stair ascends from the central foyer, flanked by the formal living and dining rooms. The informal family room, accessible from the foyer, captures the Early American style with exposed beams, wood paneling, and brick fireplace wall. A separate dinette opens to an efficient kitchen. Four bedrooms and a two-basin family bath, arranged around the central hall, occupy the second floor.

First floor — 1,023 sq. ft.
Second floor — 923 sq. ft.
(optional slab construction available)

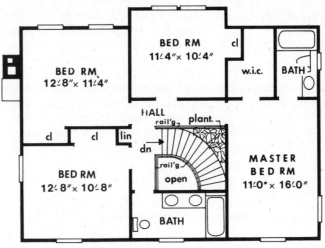

BED RM
11'-4" × 10'-4"   cl

BED RM
12'-8" × 11'-4"   w.i.c.   BATH

cl   cl   lin

HALL
rail'g   plant.

dn

BED RM
12'-8" × 10'-8"   rail'g   open   MASTER BED RM
11'-0" × 16'-0"

BATH

SECOND FLOOR PLAN

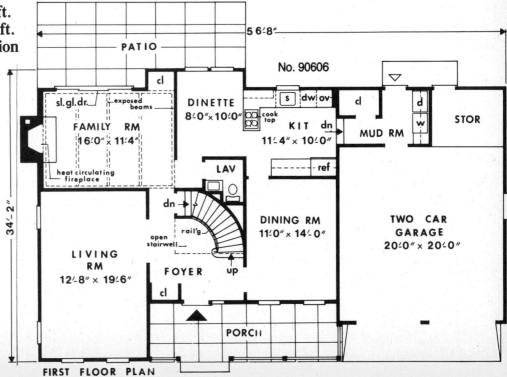

PATIO

56'-8"

No. 90606

cl

sl. gl. dr.   exposed beams   DINETTE
8'-0" × 10'-0"   cook top   s   dw   ov   cl   d   STOR

FAMILY RM
16'-0" × 11'-4"   KIT
11'-4" × 10'-0"   dn   MUD RM   w

heat circulating fireplace   LAV   ref

34'-2"   dn   rail'g   DINING RM
11'-0" × 14'-0"   TWO CAR GARAGE
20'-0" × 20'-0"

open stairwell

LIVING RM
12'-8" × 19'-6"   FOYER   up

cl

PORCH

FIRST FLOOR PLAN

Surround Yourself with Luxury

No. 10615

A magnificent home in every detail, this stately 5 bedroom residence surrounds you with thoughtful luxury. Enter the oversized, tiled foyer and view the grand staircase whose landing splits the ascent into separate wings and creates an aura of privacy for a guest or live-in relative in bedroom 4. Serenity reigns throughout the home thanks to the courtyard plan that insulates the master bedroom complex and bedroom 2 from the main living areas. The kitchen is designed to serve the eating areas and family room and reserve the vast living room for more formal entertaining. Most of the home shares access to, and wonderful views of, the patio, covered by the 2nd floor deck, and pool area.

First floor — 4,075 sq. ft.
Second floor — 1,179 sq. ft.
Garage — 633 sq. ft.

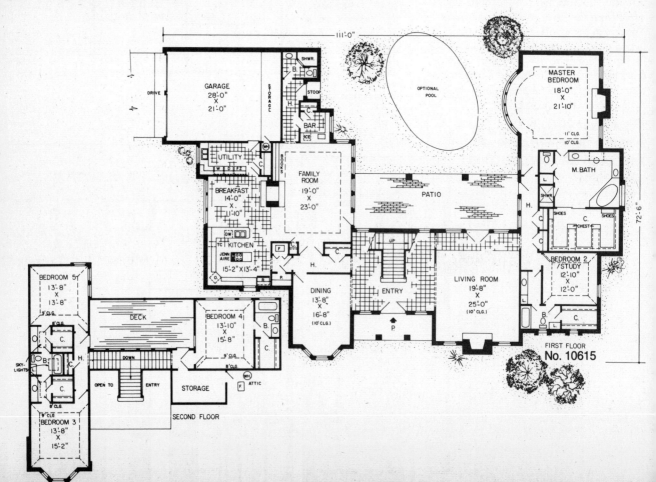

Open Plan Brightens Compact Dwelling

No. 90506

Open to the balcony above and the entry and dining room below, the vaulted great room is the highlight of this home. A central staircase winds its way up to three bedrooms, two baths, and a play room that doubles as storage. The master bedroom and breakfast nook feature bay windows that give both rooms a distinctive shape and cheerful atmosphere.

**First floor — 996 sq. ft.
Second floor — 942 sq. ft.**

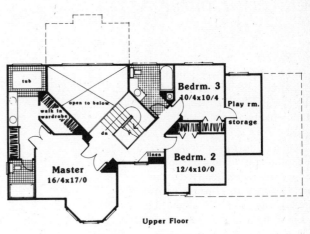

tub

walk in wardrobe

open to below

Bedrm. 3
10/4x10/4

Play rm.

storage

dn

linen

Bedrm. 2
12/4x10/0

Master
16/4x17/0

Upper Floor

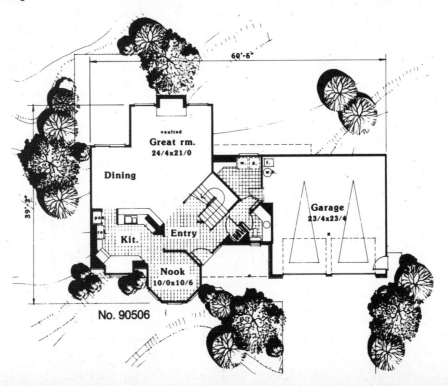

60'-6"

vaulted
Great rm.
24/4x21/0

Dining

39'-3"

w. d.

Garage
23/4x23/4

Kit.

Entry

Nook
10/0x10/6

No. 90506

Den Can Double As a Home Office

No. 90816

Traditional styling marks this elegant, four-bedroom home with lots of outdoor living space. Flooded with light from a picture window, the sunken living room lies just off the central foyer. At the rear of the home, the kitchen is flanked by the formal dining room and a breakfast nook. Sliding glass doors open to the sundeck. A single step leads down to the fireplaced family room. Window gables at the top of the gently curving staircase provide pleasing study nooks. The master suite features a luxurious whirlpool bath.

First floor — 1,252 sq. ft.
Second floor — 1,117 sq. ft.
Unfinished basement — 1,245 sq. ft.
Garage — 564 sq. ft.
Width — 71 ft.
Depth — 35 ft.(plus 8 ft. sundeck)

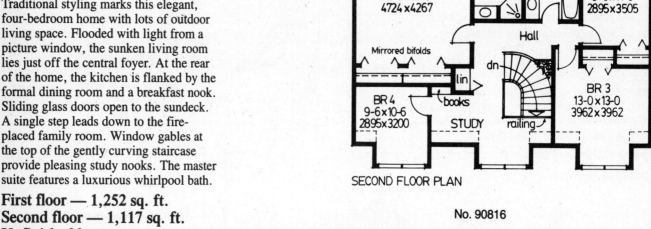

SECOND FLOOR PLAN

No. 90816

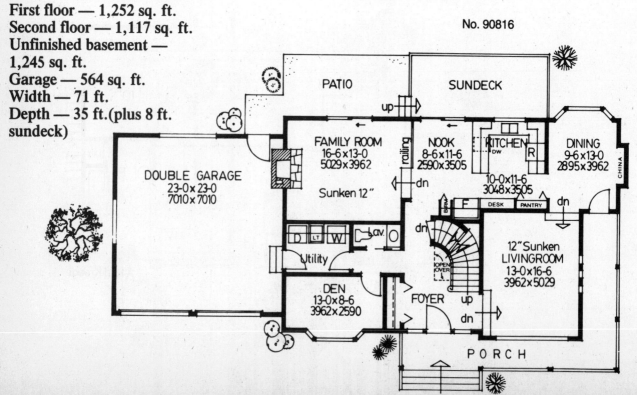

Comfortable Contemporary Design

No. 10567

This simple but well designed contemporary expresses comfort and offers a lot of options normally found in larger designs. On the first level, a front kitchen is offered with an open, non-partitioned dining area. Two bedrooms are located on the first floor. The living room sports a skylight, adding more natural lighting to the room, and has a prefabricated wood-burning fireplace. The second floor has a secluded master bedroom with a sitting room, walk-in closets, and a full bath. Other features include a two-car garage and a brick patio.

First floor — 1,046 sq. ft.
Second floor — 375 sq. ft.
Basement — 1,046 sq. ft.
Garage — 472 sq. ft.

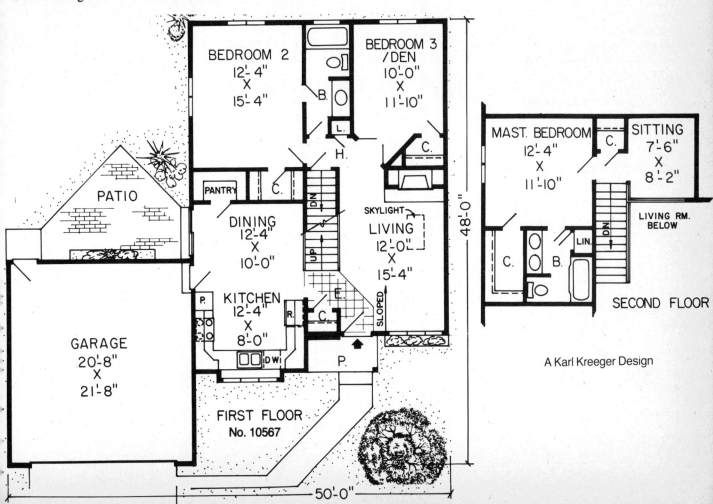

A Karl Kreeger Design

Delightful Living Every Day

No. 10429

The striking exterior of this two story design features transom glass, patterned brick, and rough cedar battens, posts and brackets. Inside, abundant space is supplied to satisify a great variety of family needs. Four bedrooms and three baths allow for a large or growing family or for numerous guests, if you prefer. Outdoor recreation areas are found on both levels: a covered patio flanked by nook, family room and living room on the first floor; and a covered balcony accessible to two bedrooms on the second floor. Openness of design has been incorporated into the kitchen/nook and living room/entry areas.

First floor — 2,270 sq. ft.
Second floor — 652 sq. ft.
Garage — 486 sq. ft.

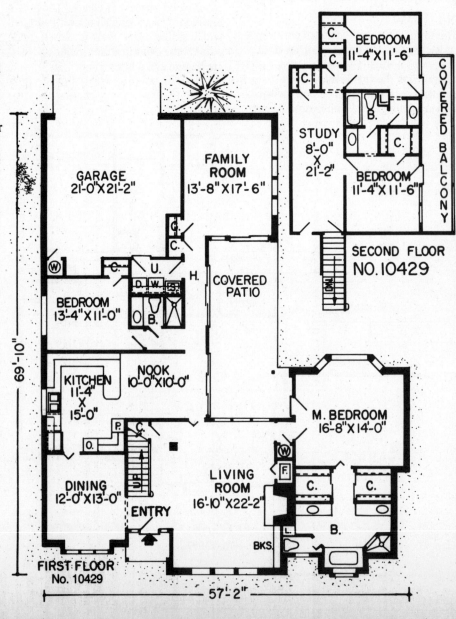

GARAGE 21'-0"X21'-2"

FAMILY ROOM 13'-8"X17'-6"

BEDROOM 13'-4"X11'-0"

COVERED PATIO

KITCHEN 11'-4" X 15'-0"

NOOK 10'-0"X10'-0"

DINING 12'-0"X13'-0"

ENTRY

LIVING ROOM 16'-10"X22'-2"

M. BEDROOM 16'-8"X14'-0"

BKS.

FIRST FLOOR No. 10429

69'-10"

57'-2"

BEDROOM 11'-4"X11'-6"

STUDY 8'-0" X 21'-2"

BEDROOM 11'-4"X11'-6"

COVERED BALCONY

SECOND FLOOR NO. 10429

Balcony Overlooks Living Room Below

No. 90356

Smaller houses are getting better all the time, not only in their exterior character and scale, but in their use of spacial volumes and interior finish materials. Here a modest two story gains importance, impact, and perceived value from the sweeping roof lines that make it look larger than it really is. Guests will be impressed by the impact of the vaulted ceiling in the living room up to the balcony hall above, the easy flow of traffic and space in the kitchen and dining areas. Note too, the luxurious master bedroom suite with a window seat bay, walk-in closet, dressing area, and private shower.

Main floor — 674 sq. ft.
Upper floor — 677 sq. ft.

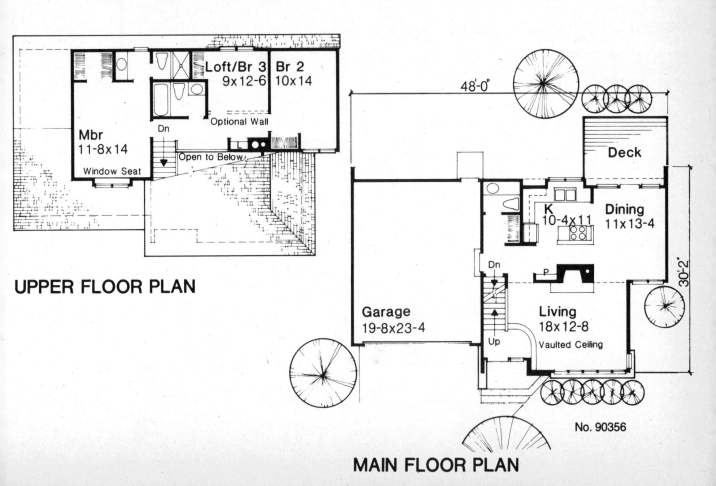

UPPER FLOOR PLAN

Mbr
11-8x14
Window Seat

Loft/Br 3
9x12-6

Br 2
10x14

Optional Wall

Dn

Open to Below

48'-0"

Deck

K
10-4x11

Dining
11x13-4

30'-2"

Garage
19-8x23-4

Dn

P

Up

Living
18x12-8
Vaulted Ceiling

No. 90356

MAIN FLOOR PLAN

Master Suite Crowns Plan

No. 10394

The master bedroom suite occupies the entire second level of this passive solar design. The living room rises two stories in the front, as does the foyer, and can be opened to the master suite to aid in air circulation. Skylights in the sloping ceilings of the kitchen and master bath give abundant light to these areas. Angled walls, both inside and out, lend a unique appeal. An air lock entry, 2X6 exterior studs, 6-inch concrete floor, and generous use of insulation help make this an energy efficient design.

First floor — 1,306 sq. ft.
Second floor — 472 sq. ft.
Garage — 576 sq. ft.

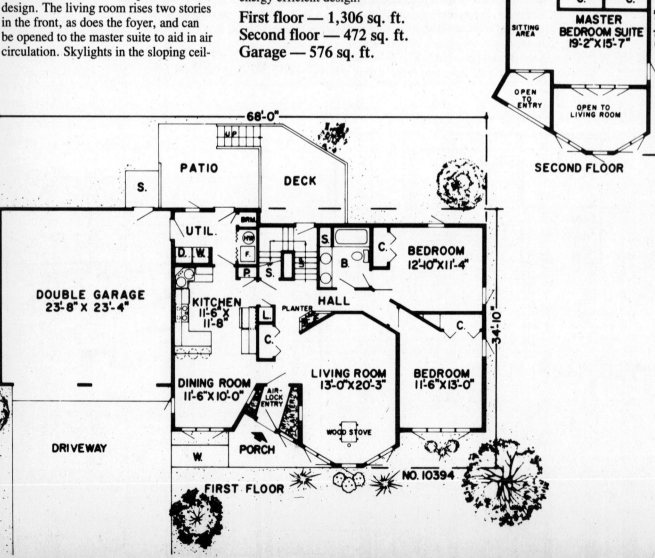

54

Bay Windows and Skylights Brighten this Tudor Home

No. 10673

Step from the arched fieldstone porch into the two-story foyer, and you can see that this traditional four bedroom home possesses a wealth of modern elements. Behind double doors lie the library and fireplaced living room, bathed in sunlight from two skylights in the sloping roof. Step out to the brick patio from the laundry room or bay windowed breakfast room. For ultimate relaxation, the master bedroom suite contains a whirlpool tub. One bedroom boasts bay windows; another features a huge walk-in closet over the two car garage.

First floor — 1,265 sq. ft.
Second floor — 1,210 sq. ft.
Basement — 1,247 sq. ft.
Garage — 506 sq. ft.

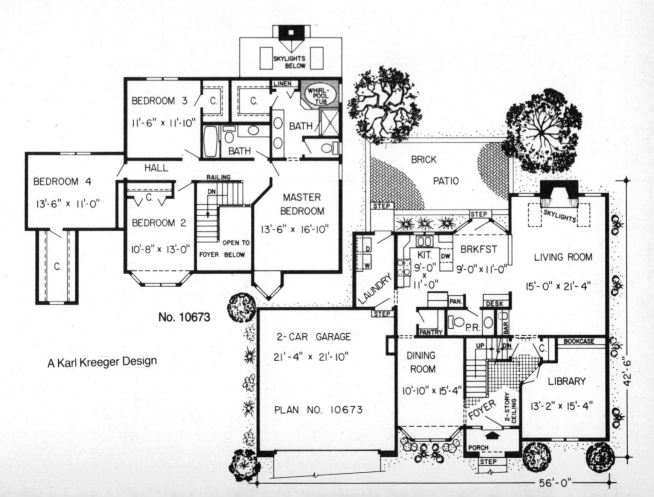

No. 10673

A Karl Kreeger Design

BEDROOM 3
11'-6" x 11'-10"

BEDROOM 4
13'-6" x 11'-0"

HALL

BEDROOM 2
10'-8" x 13'-0"

OPEN TO FOYER BELOW

RAILING

DN

SKYLIGHTS BELOW

LINEN

BATH

BATH

WHIRL-POOL TUB

MASTER BEDROOM
13'-6" x 16'-10"

BRICK PATIO

2-CAR GARAGE
21'-4" x 21'-10"

PLAN NO. 10673

LAUNDRY

KIT.
9'-0" x 11'-0"

BRKFST
9'-0" x 11'-0"

PAN.

PANTRY

P.R.

DESK

BAR

LIVING ROOM
15'-0" x 21'-4"

SKYLIGHTS

BOOKCASE

DINING ROOM
10'-10" x 15'-4"

UP

DN

C.

FOYER

2-STORY CEILING

LIBRARY
13'-2" x 15'-4"

PORCH

STEP

42'-6"

56'-0"

Cozy Cape Cod

No. 90115

This homey Cape home will blend beautifully in any setting. The formal living and dining rooms are completely separated from the family room, enabling adults and children to enjoy undisturbed everyday living. Notice the location of the first floor bath in relation to the din-

ing room —a plan feature that permits this room to be used as a first floor bedroom, if desired. Back service entrance, mud room and laundry convenient to the kitchen are favorable points of the plan, too. On the second floor, the huge master bedroom has its own dressing area and entrance to the vanity bath.

First floor — 1,068 sq. ft.
Second floor — 804 sq. ft.

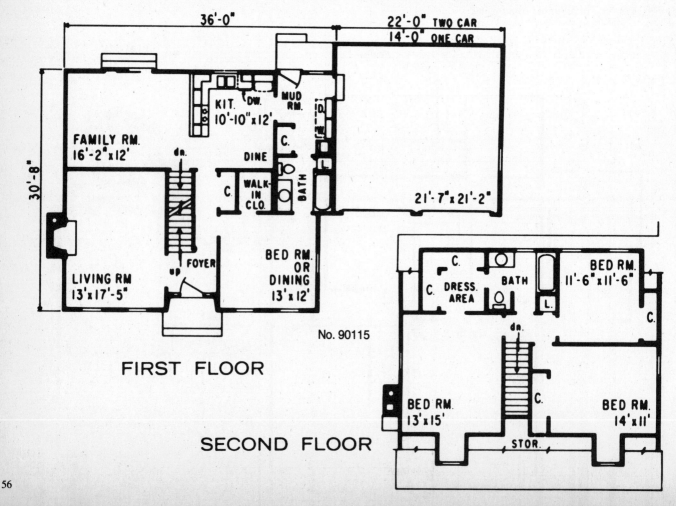

No. 90115

FIRST FLOOR

SECOND FLOOR

Master Bedroom on First Level

No. 90142

This excellent traditional design has the master bedroom located on the first level and equipped with a walk-in closet and a large bath area that incorporates a skylight over the tub. Also on the first level is a living room with large bay windows allowing natural lighting to fill the room. The kitchen has an abundance of cabinet space and includes a pantry that has plenty of storage space. The laundry room is located just between the kitchen and garage. The second level has three bedrooms and one full bath.

First floor — 1,663 sq. ft.
Second floor — 727 sq. ft.

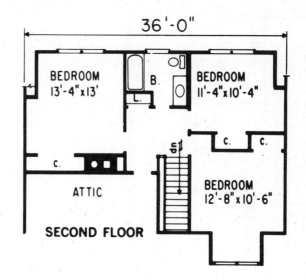

36'-0"

BEDROOM
13'-4" x 13'

B.

BEDROOM
11'-4" x 10'-4"

c.   c.

BEDROOM
12'-8" x 10'-6"

ATTIC

SECOND FLOOR

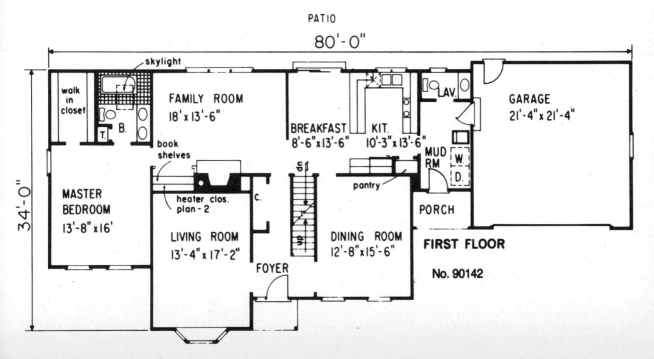

PATIO

80'-0"

34'-0"

walk in closet

skylight

B.
T.

FAMILY ROOM
18' x 13'-6"

BREAKFAST
8'-6"x13'-6"

KIT.
10'-3" x 13'-6"

LAV.

GARAGE
21'-4" x 21'-4"

MASTER BEDROOM
13'-8" x 16'

book shelves

heater clos.
plan - 2

c.

pantry

MUD RM

W. D.

LIVING ROOM
13'-4" x 17'-2"

DINING ROOM
12'-8"x15'-6"

PORCH

FIRST FLOOR

FOYER

No. 90142

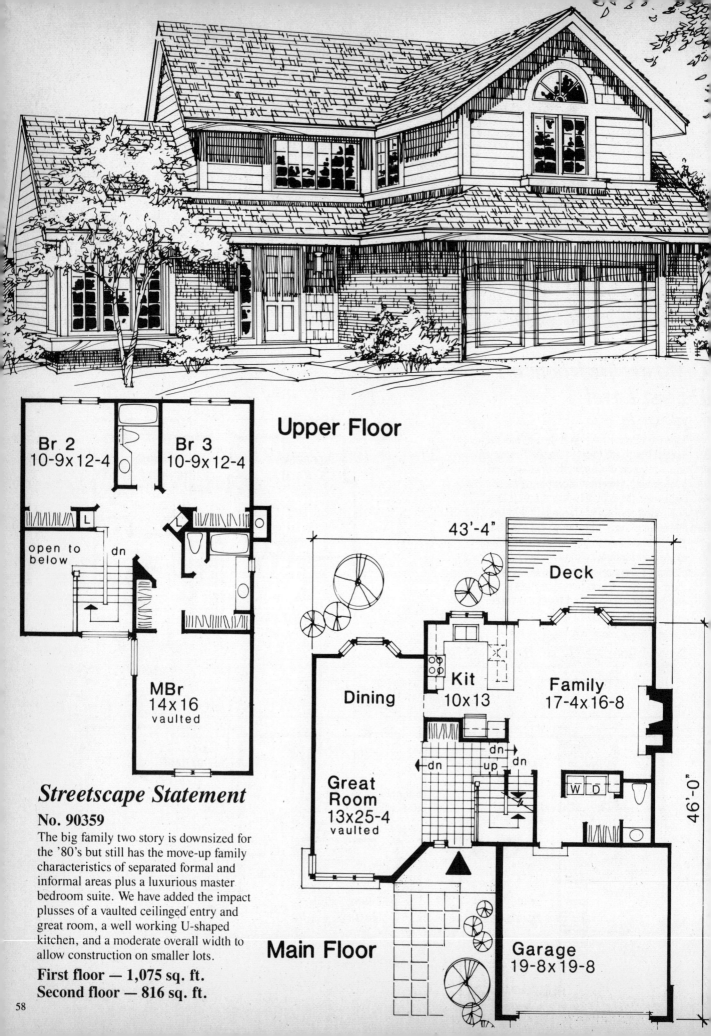

Upper Floor

Br 2
10-9x12-4

Br 3
10-9x12-4

open to below

dn

MBr
14x16
vaulted

Streetscape Statement

No. 90359

The big family two story is downsized for the '80's but still has the move-up family characteristics of separated formal and informal areas plus a luxurious master bedroom suite. We have added the impact plusses of a vaulted ceilinged entry and great room, a well working U-shaped kitchen, and a moderate overall width to allow construction on smaller lots.

First floor — 1,075 sq. ft.
Second floor — 816 sq. ft.

43'-4"

Deck

Dining

Kit
10x13

Family
17-4x16-8

Great Room
13x25-4
vaulted

dn   dn
dn   up

W D

46'-0"

Garage
19-8x19-8

Main Floor

Old American Saltbox Design

No. 90123

A sloping ceiling creates a sense of spaciousness for this modest design. Relax in front of the centrally located fireplace in cool weather or move through triple sliding glass doors to the roomy deck when weather is warmer. Behind the living room lies a bedroom, full bath and kitchen/dining area which has a window seat. Laundry facilities are conveniently placed off the kitchen. On the left of the living room a quiet corner has been tucked under the stairs leading to the second floor. The second level affords two nice sized bedrooms (one with its own private deck), joined by a full bath. A balcony skirts the entire level and overlooks the living room below.

First floor — 840 sq. ft.
Second floor — 440 sq. ft.

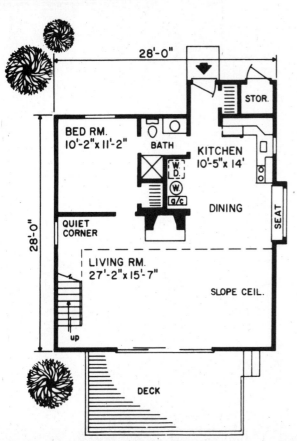

FIRST FLOOR

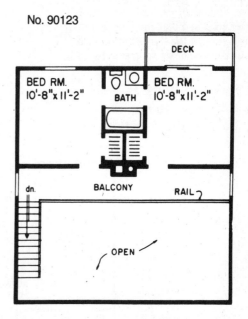

No. 90123

SECOND FLOOR

Year Round Retreat

No. 90613

This compact home is a bargain to build and designed to save on energy bills. Large glass areas face south, and the dramatic sloping ceiling of the living room allows heat from the wood-burning stove to rise into the upstairs bedrooms through high louvers on the inside wall. In hot weather, just open the windows on both floors for cooling air circulation. Sliding glass doors in the kitchen and living rooms open to the deck for outdoor dining or relaxation. One bedroom and a full bath complete the first floor. A stair off the foyer ends in a balcony with a commanding view of the living room. Two spacious bedrooms are separated by a full bath.

First floor — 917 sq. ft.
Second floor — 465 sq. ft.
(optional slab construction available)

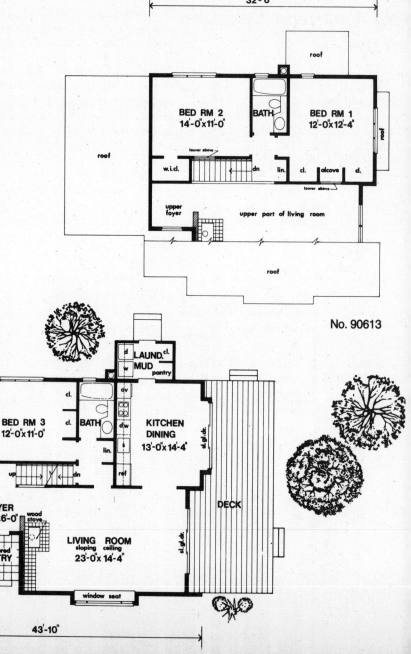

No. 90613

Facade Hints at Distinctive Interior

No. 20091

Stand in the foyer of this elegant master-piece that combines beauty and convenience. To your left, there's a vaulted formal dining room. To your right, behind double doors, lies the library with its built-in bookcase wall. Straight ahead in the family room, the massive fireplace is flanked by window walls for a view of the deck and rear yard. And, don't forget to look up at the balcony that links three huge bedrooms, including the vaulted master suite with its skylit bath. Notice the pass-through convenience between the island kitchen and family room, the adjacent, sunwashed breakfast room, the pantry and utility room just off the garage entry, and the handy first-floor powder room.

First floor — 1,556 sq. ft.
Second floor — 1,121 sq. ft.
Basement — 1,556 sq. ft.

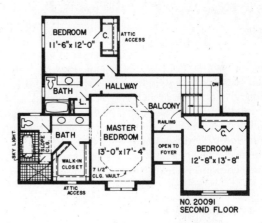

NO. 20091
SECOND FLOOR

No. 20091

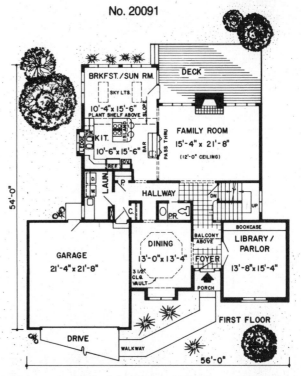

FIRST FLOOR

A Karl Kreeger Design

Salt Box Design
Boast Plant Haven

No. 10368

Extended wood beams, shake shingles and wood siding give a warm, homey character to the exterior of this salt box design. A plant nook draws your attention in the living room. Ceilings slope upward here to meet a balcony hallway above. Upstairs bedrooms each have

their own bath and the rear bedroom enjoys its own balcony. The homemaker will find the location of the washer and dryer in the kitchen, behind wood folding doors, a real step and time saver. Two patios for relaxing and dining are close at hand also; one through sliding doors from the family room and the other off the dining room. An air lock entry with a coat closet, guards against the infiltration of adverse weather.

First floor — 1,427 sq. ft.
Second floor — 674 sq. ft.
Basement — 1,175 sq. ft.
Garage — 576 sq. ft.

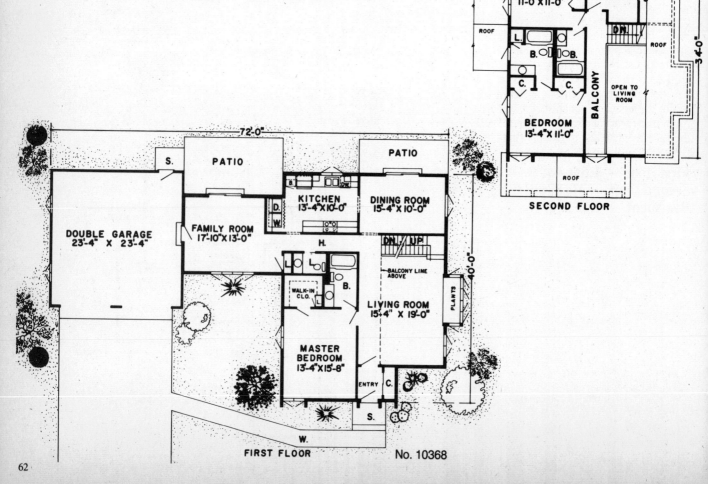

Traditional Sun Catcher

No. 20096

Windows and skylights in all shapes and sizes give this airy home a cozy feeling. From the two-story foyer to the skylit breakfast nook off the island kitchen, active areas are arranged in an open plan just perfect for entertaining. In warm weather, you'll enjoy the huge rear deck, accessible from both the living and breakfast rooms. Overnight guests will appreciate the full bath adjoining the downstairs den. Upstairs, three bedrooms open to a balcony overlooking the floor below. Look at the master suite. A walk-in closet and shower, double vanities, and a raised, skylit tub make this spacious area a luxurious retreat.

First floor — 1,286 sq. ft.
Second floor — 957 sq. ft.

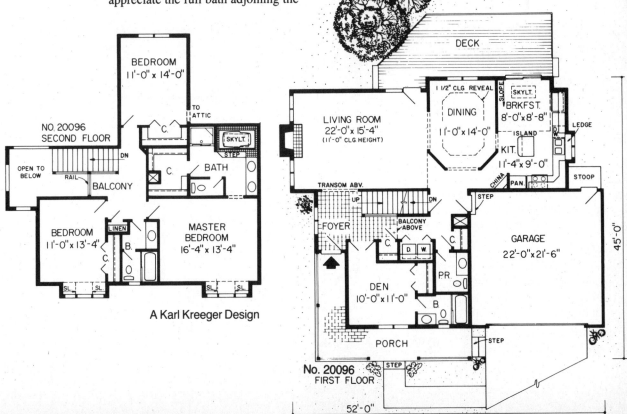

A Karl Kreeger Design

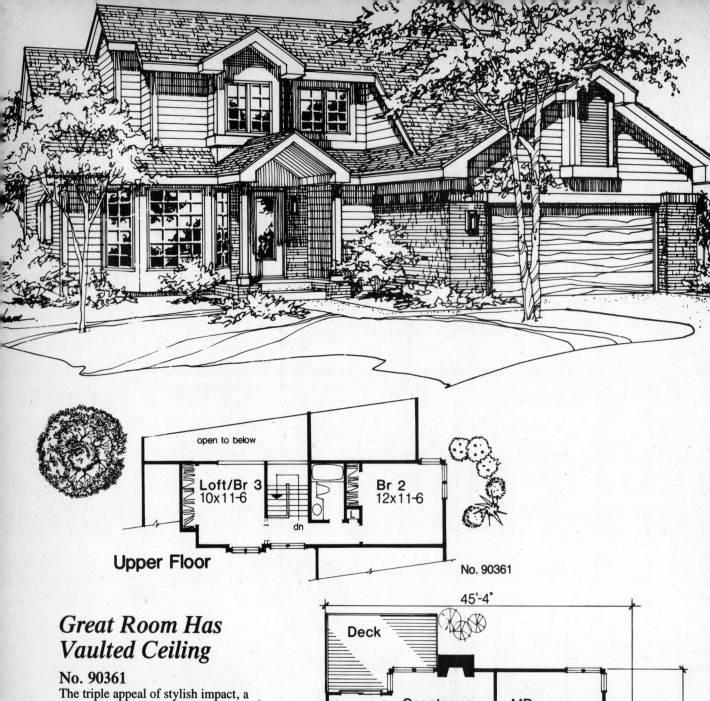

Upper Floor

open to below

Loft/Br 3
10x11-6

Br 2
12x11-6

dn

No. 90361

Great Room Has Vaulted Ceiling

No. 90361

The triple appeal of stylish impact, a great kitchen with charming breakfast area, and a luxurious master bedroom suite give this house high perceived value in today's very competitive mid-priced marketplace. Note how these features are emphasized with balconied stair overlooking living and dining rooms, greenhouse plus bay windowed kitchen, and master bath with platform tub, stall shower, and oversized walk-in closet. Combined with the highly detailed, custom-look exterior, this total design package gives you a lot for your money.

First floor — 1,105 sq. ft.
Second floor — 460 sq. ft.

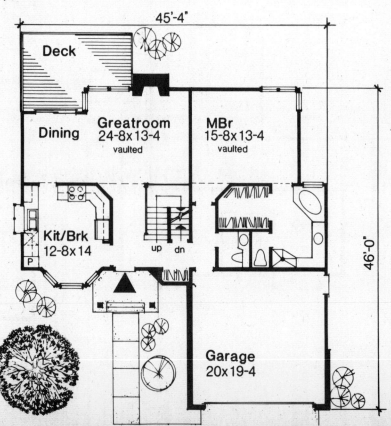

45'-4"

Deck

Dining

Greatroom
24-8x13-4
vaulted

MBr
15-8x13-4
vaulted

Kit/Brk
12-8x14

P

up   dn

46'-0"

Garage
20x19-4

Master Suite Crowns Outstanding Plan

No. 10334

Here's a fabulous executive home. Incorporating a study, walk-in closet, and lavish bath with whirlpool, shower, and skylight, the master suite adds a finishing touch to this exceptional home. The deck-edged main level details an eye-catching 25-ft. oak floored great room with bow window. Also outlined are two bedrooms, a slate floored dining room, and kitchen with pantry and snack island. On the basement level, the family room joins the patio via sliding glass doors, and a fourth bedroom and extra bath are included.

Main level — 1,742 sq. ft.
Upper level — 809 sq. ft.
Lower level — 443 sq. ft.
Basement — 1,270 sq. ft.
Garage — 558 sq. ft.

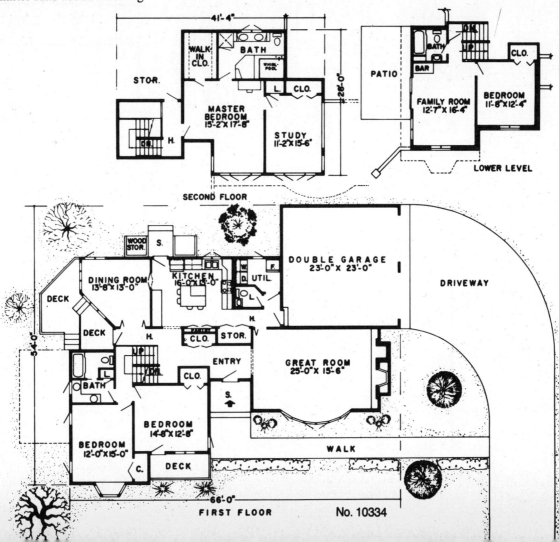

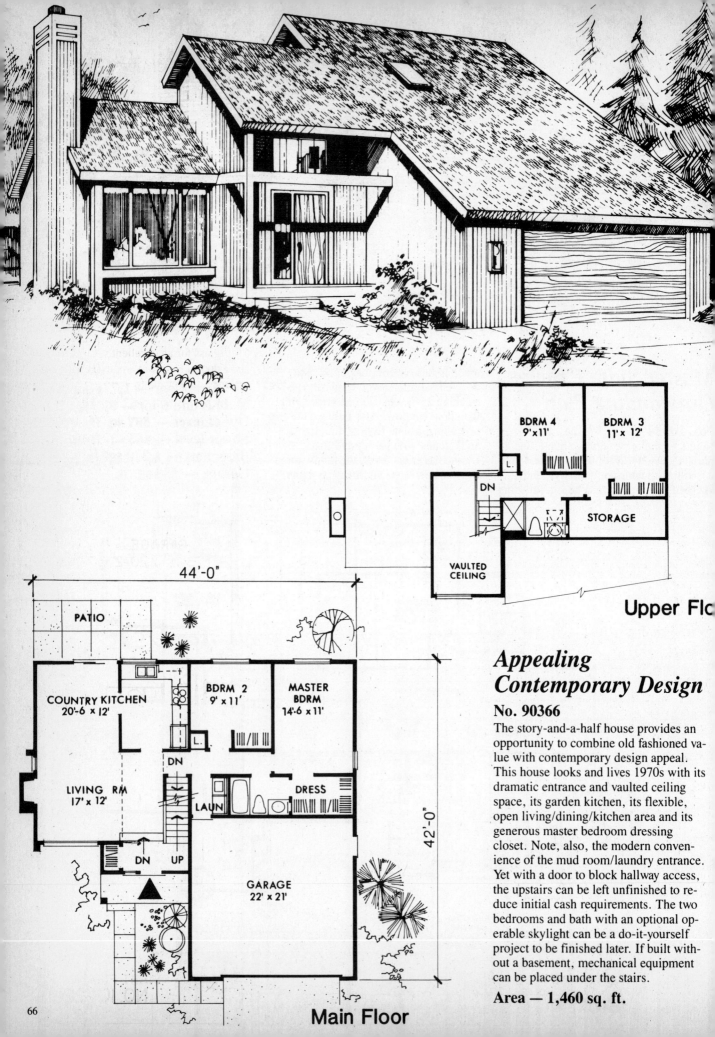

BDRM 4
9' x 11'

BDRM 3
11' x 12'

DN

STORAGE

VAULTED
CEILING

Upper Flo

44'-0"

PATIO

COUNTRY KITCHEN
20'-6 x 12'

BDRM 2
9' x 11'

MASTER
BDRM
14'-6 x 11'

DN

LIVING RM
17' x 12'

LAUN

DRESS

DN   UP

GARAGE
22' x 21'

42'-0"

Appealing
Contemporary Design

No. 90366

The story-and-a-half house provides an opportunity to combine old fashioned value with contemporary design appeal. This house looks and lives 1970s with its dramatic entrance and vaulted ceiling space, its garden kitchen, its flexible, open living/dining/kitchen area and its generous master bedroom dressing closet. Note, also, the modern convenience of the mud room/laundry entrance. Yet with a door to block hallway access, the upstairs can be left unfinished to reduce initial cash requirements. The two bedrooms and bath with an optional operable skylight can be a do-it-yourself project to be finished later. If built without a basement, mechanical equipment can be placed under the stairs.

Area — 1,460 sq. ft.

Main Floor

Exquisite Tudor

No. 10422

From the stucco and rough cedar battens to the brick quoins and leaded windows, the styling of this Tudor is exquisite. Brickwork on the chimney and around windows is varied to add further elegance to the exterior. The garage is located in the rear, keeping the front of the home unbroken by garage doors. A large mas-

ter bedroom on the lower level featuring a luxury bath and large walk-in closet, three additional bedrooms on the upper level, and 3 1/2 baths provide plenty of room for a growing family or guests. Both a living room and family room are shown, the living room with fireplace and sliding glass doors to the covered patio, and the family room with bar, patio access, and one complete wall of

glass for an excellent view of the outdoors.

First floor — 1,776 sq. ft.
Second floor — 776 sq. ft.
Garage — 557 sq. ft.
Patio & Porch — 228 sq. ft.

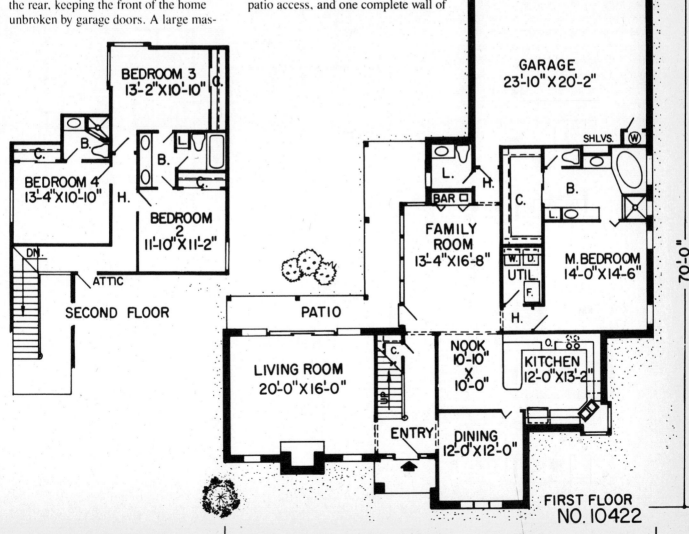

Three Bedroom Features Cathedral Ceilings

No. 20051

The tiled foyer of this charming house rises to the second floor balcony and is lighted by a circular window. To the right of the foyer are the powder room, the compact laundry area, and the entrance to the well-designed kitchen. The kitchen features a central island, built-in desk, pantry, and adjacent breakfast area. The combined living and dining room enjoys a fireplace, built-in bookcase, and sloped ceiling.

First floor — 1,285 sq. ft.
Second floor — 490 sq. ft.
Basement — 1,285 sq. ft.
Garage — 495 sq. ft.

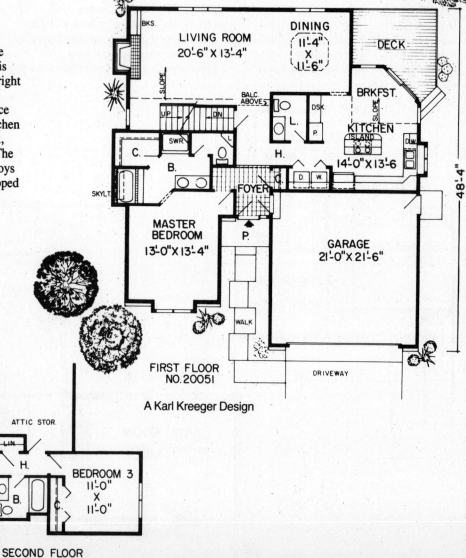

FIRST FLOOR
NO. 20051

A Karl Kreeger Design

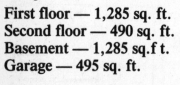

SECOND FLOOR

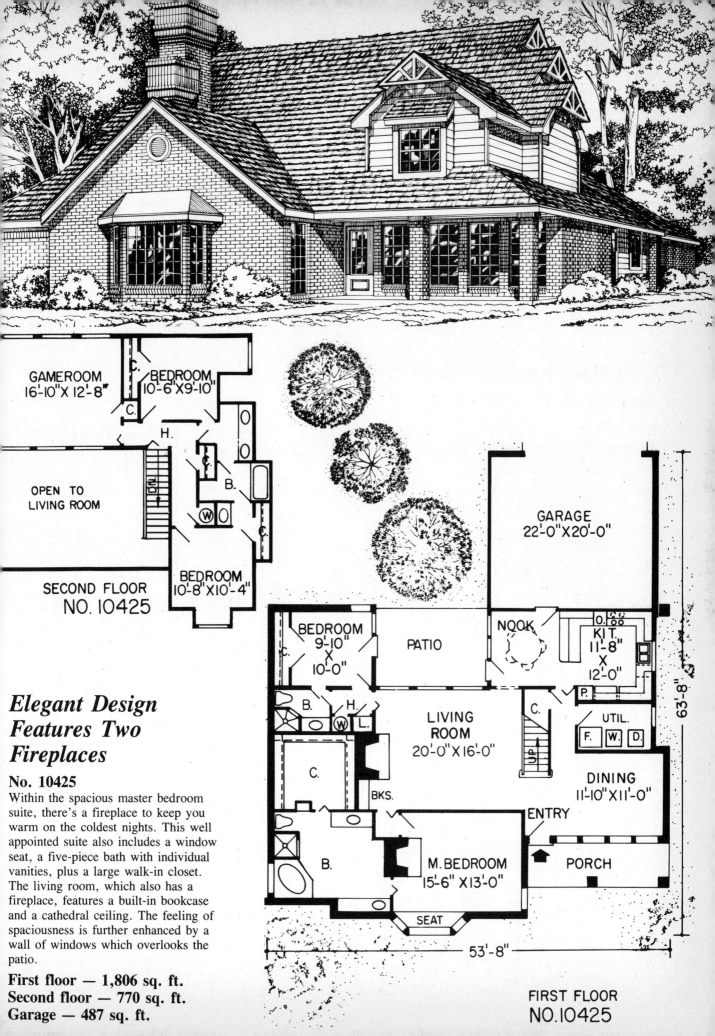

GAMEROOM
16'-10"X 12'-8"

BEDROOM
10'-6"X9'-10"

C.

C.

H.

C.

B.

W

OPEN TO
LIVING ROOM

BEDROOM
10'-8"X10'-4"

C.

SECOND FLOOR
NO. 10425

GARAGE
22'-0"X20'-0"

BEDROOM
9'-10"
X
10'-0"

PATIO

NOOK

KIT.
11'-8"
X
12'-0"

C.

B.

H.

W

L.

P.

UTIL.

F. W. D.

LIVING
ROOM
20'-0"X16'-0"

C.

C.

BKS.

DINING
11'-10"X11'-0"

ENTRY

M. BEDROOM
15'-6" X13'-0"

B.

PORCH

SEAT

63'-8"

53'-8"

Elegant Design Features Two Fireplaces

No. 10425

Within the spacious master bedroom suite, there's a fireplace to keep you warm on the coldest nights. This well appointed suite also includes a window seat, a five-piece bath with individual vanities, plus a large walk-in closet. The living room, which also has a fireplace, features a built-in bookcase and a cathedral ceiling. The feeling of spaciousness is further enhanced by a wall of windows which overlooks the patio.

First floor — 1,806 sq. ft.
Second floor — 770 sq. ft.
Garage — 487 sq. ft.

FIRST FLOOR
NO. 10425

Master Bedroom at Entry Level

No. 20060

Striking angles best describes this contemporary design. At the front entrance, an attractive half-circle window transom is built above the door. Through the foyer, the kitchen is centered perfectly between the breakfast area and a more formal dining area. The breakfast room leads onto a very large wooden deck through sliding glass doors. From the breakfast room, the living room comes complete with a burning fireplace, plus the extra feature of a sloping, open beamed ceiling. This design offers the master bedroom on the entry level, with a dressing area, walk-in closet, and full bath. The second level offers two bedrooms with a full bath and a convenient cedar closet.

First floor — 1,279 sq. ft.
Second floor — 502 sq. ft.
Basement — 729 sq. ft.
Garage — 470 sq. ft.

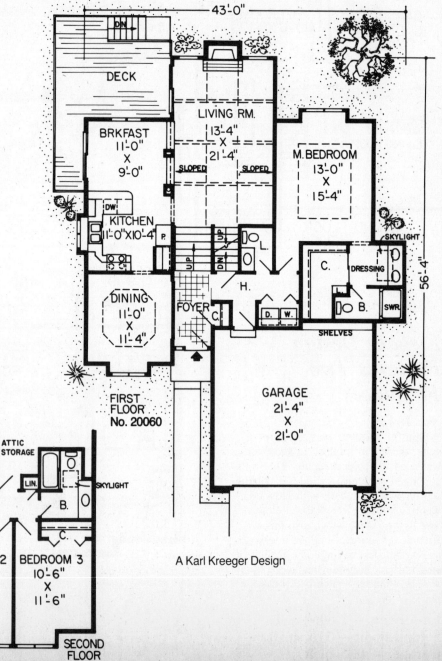

A Karl Kreeger Design

Sunlight Floods Every Room

No. 90511

Walk into the two-story foyer from the garage or sheltered front entry and you'll be struck by the wide-open spaciousness of this compact home. The kitchen is flanked by vaulted living and dining rooms on one side and a fireplaced fam-ily room and breakfast nook on the other. Atop the open stairs, the plush master bedroom suite lies behind double doors. Two additional bedrooms share an adjoining full bath.

First floor — 1,078 sq. ft.
Second floor — 974 sq. ft.

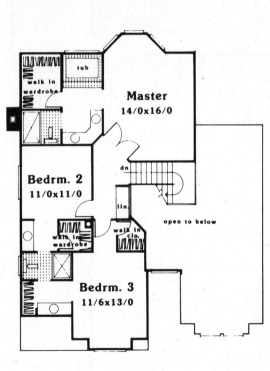

Upper Floor

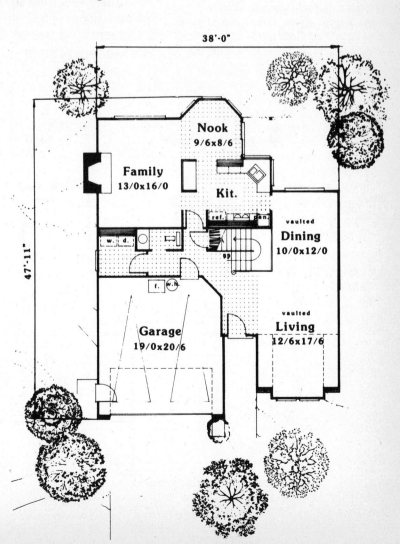

Enjoy the Backyard Views

No. 10550

There's lots of room for your growing family in this four bedroom Tudor beauty. Recessed ceilings in the dining room and master bedroom suite, a vaulted front office, and a beamed great room give first floor living areas distinctive angles. And, the sunporch off the breakfast nook is a warm place to curl up even on the coldest day. You'll never have to worry about traffic jams on busy weekday mornings. With two full baths upstairs and two convenient lavatories on the first floor, everyone can get out on time.

First floor — 2,069 sq. ft.
Second floor — 821 sq. ft.
Basement — 2,045 sq. ft.
Garage — 562 sq. ft.

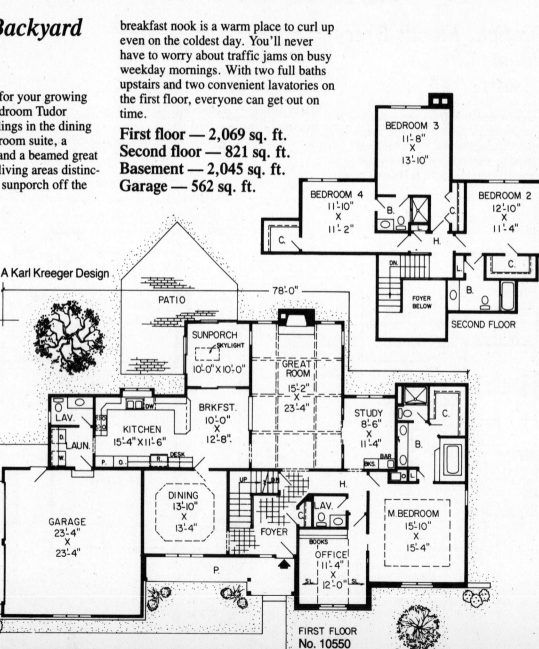

Elegant Exterior Enhanced by Luxury Features

No. 10511

The large, first floor master suite of this elegant home not only includes a spacious five-piece bath and dressing room, but also incorporates a walk-in closet, a full wall closet and a private entrance to the adjacent library. In addition to the library there is also a den which could be used as a guest bedroom. The living room, with its fireplace, bar and bow window, is separated from the more informal areas by tiled hallways. The tiled areas lead to the tiled kitchen and dining rooms as well as to the family room. Separated from these living areas are the three bedrooms on the second floor. These comfortable rooms share a large, four-piece bath.

First floor — 2,006 sq. ft.
Second floor — 894 sq. ft.
Garage — 568 sq. ft.

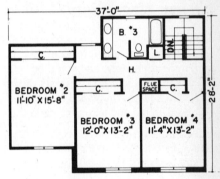

SECOND FLOOR

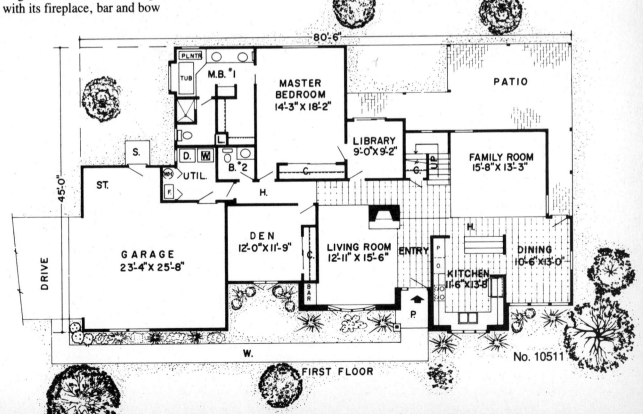

FIRST FLOOR

No. 10511

Enjoy the View

No. 20095

Step into the sunwashed foyer of this contemporary beauty, and you'll be faced with a choice. You can walk downstairs into a huge, fireplaced rec room with built-in bar and adjoining patio.

Three bedrooms and a full bath complete the lower level. Or, you can ascend the stairs to a massive living room with sloping ceilings, a tiled fireplace, and a commanding view of the back yard. Sharing the view, the breakfast nook with sunny bay opens to an outdoor deck. The adjoining kitchen is just steps away from

the formal dining room, which features recessed ceilings and overlooks the foyer. You'll also find the master suite on this level, just past the powder room off the living room.

Upper level — 1,448 sq. ft.
Lower level — 1,029 sq. ft.
Garage — 504 sq. ft.

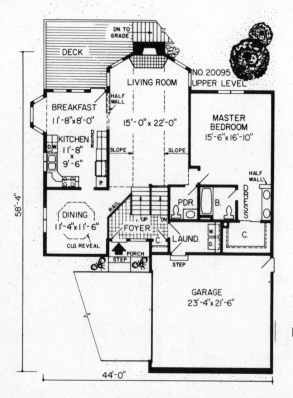

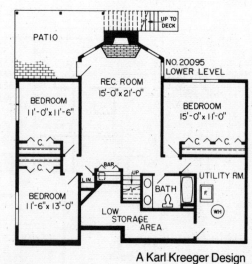

A Karl Kreeger Design

No. 20095

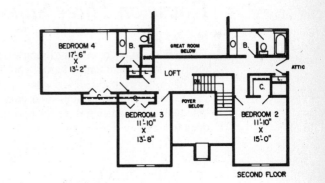

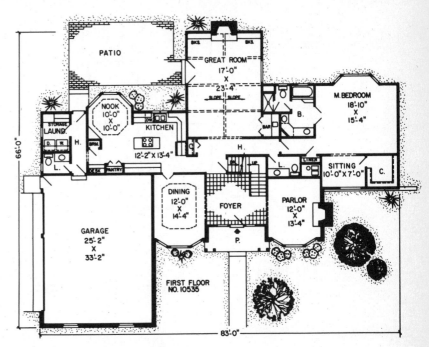

Bridge Over Foyer Introduces Unique Features Of Four-bedroom

No. 10535

The dramatic, two-story foyer opens into a cathedral-ceilinged great room, complete with a cozy fireplace that is framed with built-in bookcases. On either side of the foyer are the parlor and the formal dining room. The spacious kitchen is completely equipped and even has an octagonal breakfast nook tucked into a bank of windows. The first-floor master bedroom boasts a quaint, but roomy sitting room. Three more bedrooms, two baths and a loft with a view of both the great room and the foyer are located on the second floor.

First floor—2,335 sq. ft.
Second floor—1,157 sq. ft.
Basement—2,281 sq. ft.
Garage—862 sq. ft.

A Karl Kreeger Design

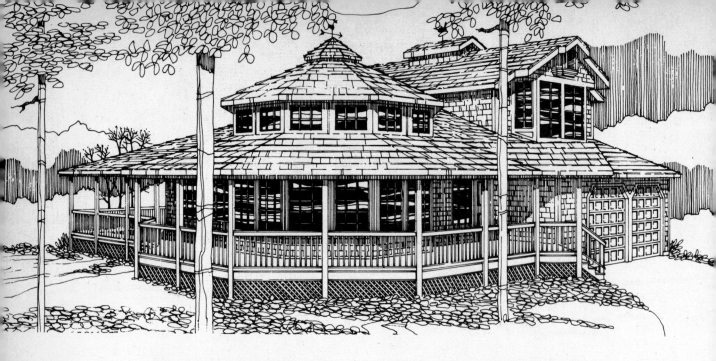

Deck Surrounds House on Three Sides

No. 91304

Sitting in the sunken, circular living room of this elegant family home, you'll feel like you're outdoors even when you're not. Windows on four sides combine with a vaulted clerestory for a wide-open feeling you'll love year-round.

When it's warm, throw open the windows, or relax on the deck. But, when there's a chill in the air, back-to-back fireplaces keep the atmosphere toasty in the living room and adjoining great room. Even the convenient kitchen, with its bay dining nook, enjoys a back yard view. Do you sew? You'll love this roomy spot just steps away from the kitchen. Bump-out and bay windows give the three upstairs bedrooms a cheerful atmosphere, and cozy sitting nooks.

First floor — 1,372 sq. ft.
Second floor — 858 sq. ft.

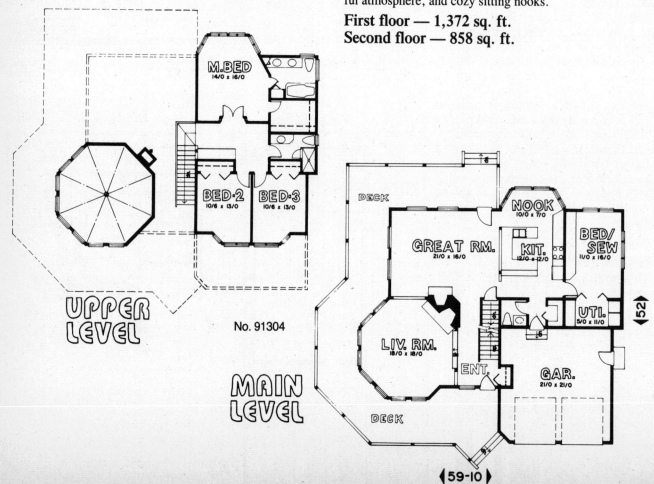

No. 91304

UPPER LEVEL

M.BED
14/0 x 16/0

BED-2
10/6 x 13/0

BED-3
10/6 x 13/0

MAIN LEVEL

DECK

GREAT RM.
21/0 x 16/0

NOOK
10/0 x 7/0

KIT.
12/0 x 12/0

BED/SEW
11/0 x 16/0

LIV. RM.
18/0 x 18/0

UTI.
5/0 x 11/0

ENT.

GAR.
21/0 x 21/0

DECK

52

59-10

Special Features Enhances Plan

No. 90365

Character is derived from the warmth of saw-textured redwood siding with natural stain and earth colored brick. Entrance features double doors and clerestory glass. Triple garage doors are sided and stained to match the siding. Central entrance gives immediate impact indoors with a two-story, open stair wall. Living room also has vaulted ceiling up to the stair landing overlook. Generous family room is stepped down for another change of spatial character. Garden kitchen and breakfast area extend indoor space to deck outside, as does greenhouse window box in dining room. Convenience and luxury features are highlighted. Note pantry and broom closets, the microwave oven, trash compactor, five-foot wet bar and first-floor laundry-mud room. Upstairs note the optional fourth bedroom or master suite retreat, attic for extra storage, oversized master bathing pool-tub and the large master closet.

Area — 2,360 sq. ft.

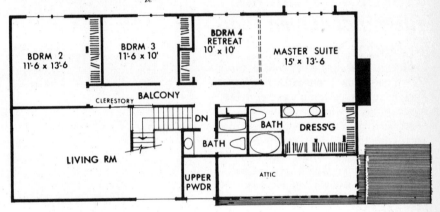

Upper Floor

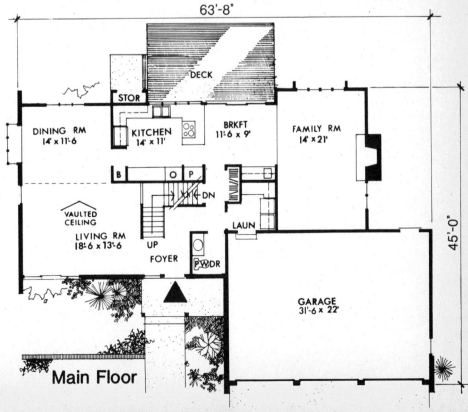

Main Floor

Two Story Windows Illuminate Open Plan

No. 10622

With built in seating and a counter top for outdoor dining convenience, a huge deck increases the warm weather living space of this airy modern home. The staircase divides the two story great room and dining room. View both rooms from the balcony above, which leads to two bedrooms and a full bath. The master bedroom with its own bath lies away from the action on the first floor.

First floor — 1,107 sq. ft.
Second floor — 497 sq. ft.

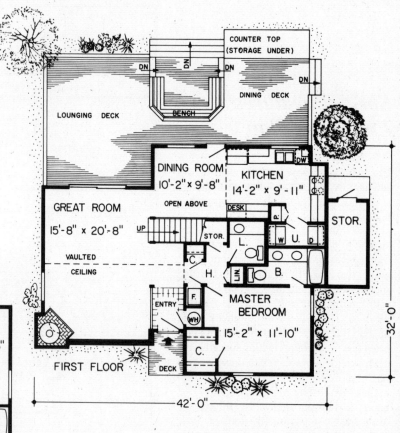

FIRST FLOOR

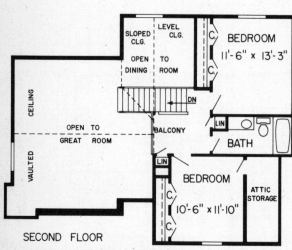

SECOND FLOOR

NO. 10622

Compact Design for a Small Lot

No. 10597

Sloping ceilings and a corner fireplace distinguish the living room of this cozy three bedroom home. Eat in the formal dining room with recessed ceiling or in the roomy kitchen, which features sliding glass doors to the patio. Walk by the laundry and pantry to the master bedroom suite. Upstairs, two bedrooms share a bath with double sinks.

First floor — 1,162 sq. ft.
Second floor — 464 sq. ft.
Basement — 1,118 sq. ft.
Garage — 450 sq. ft.

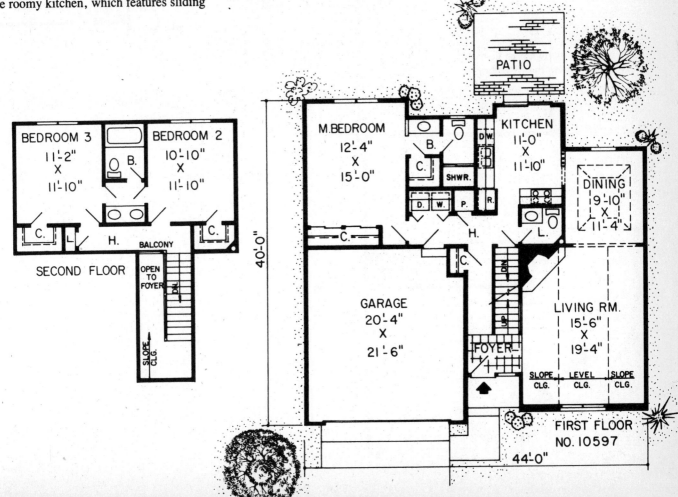

PATIO

BEDROOM 3
11'-2"
X
11'-10"

BEDROOM 2
10'-10"
X
11'-10"

B.

C.

L.

H.

BALCONY

SECOND FLOOR

OPEN TO FOYER

DN.

SLOPE CLG.

M.BEDROOM
12'-4"
X
15'-0"

KITCHEN
11'-0"
X
11'-10"

DW.

B.

C.

SHWR.

D. W. P. R.

C.

H.

L.

DINING
9'-10"
X
11'-4"

40'-0"

GARAGE
20'-4"
X
21'-6"

C.

FOYER

LIVING RM.
15'-6"
X
19'-4"

SLOPE CLG.

LEVEL CLG.

SLOPE CLG.

FIRST FLOOR
NO. 10597

44'-0"

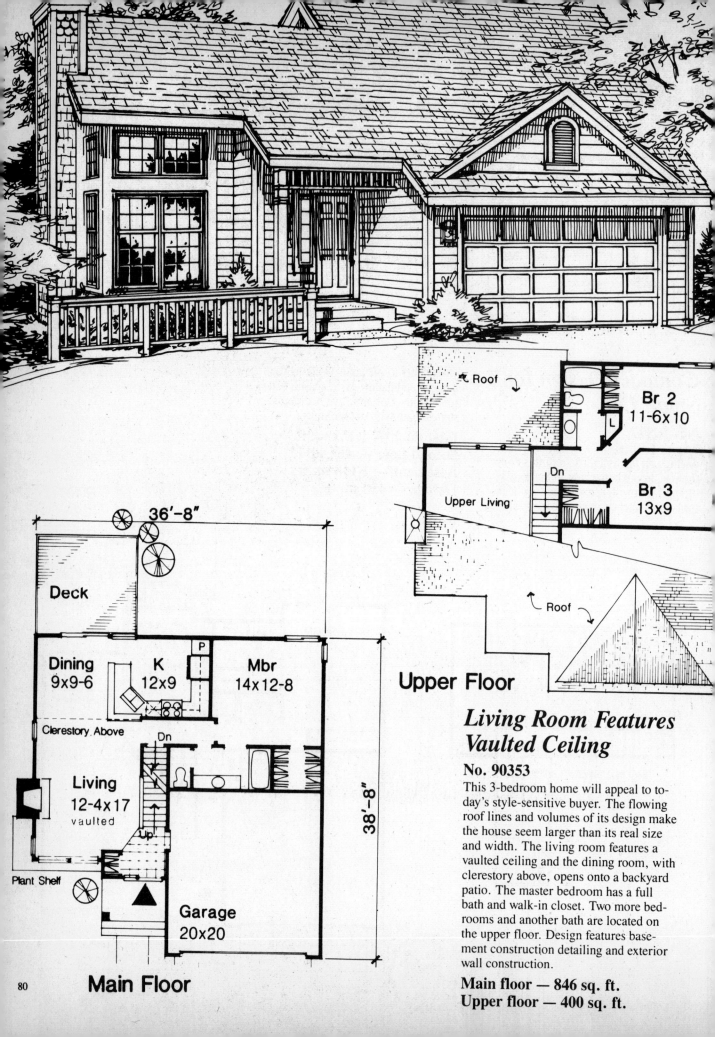

Upper Floor

Br 2
11-6x10

Br 3
13x9

Dn

Upper Living

Roof

Roof

Main Floor

36'-8"

38'-8"

Deck

Dining
9x9-6

K
12x9

P

Mbr
14x12-8

Clerestory Above

Dn

Living
12-4x17
vaulted

Up

Plant Shelf

Garage
20x20

Living Room Features Vaulted Ceiling

No. 90353

This 3-bedroom home will appeal to today's style-sensitive buyer. The flowing roof lines and volumes of its design make the house seem larger than its real size and width. The living room features a vaulted ceiling and the dining room, with clerestory above, opens onto a backyard patio. The master bedroom has a full bath and walk-in closet. Two more bedrooms and another bath are located on the upper floor. Design features basement construction detailing and exterior wall construction.

Main floor — 846 sq. ft.
Upper floor — 400 sq. ft.

At Home in a Hillside

No. 10644

The four walls won't get you down in this convenient 4 bedroom, 3 1/2 bath beauty; every room has an interesting shape! From the foyer, view the recessed ceilings of the dining room, the bump out windows of the parlor, and the fireplaced family room with patio. Beyond the central stairwell lies the angular kitchen with skylit breakfast nook. The master bedroom suite is right down a short hall. Each of the upstairs bedrooms has direct access to a full bath. And, don't worry about carrying a heavy laundry basket down the stairs. A centrally located chute delivers dirty clothes to the laundry room.

First floor — 1,593 sq. ft.
Second floor — 818 sq. ft.
Unfinished basement — 863 sq. ft.
Garage — 720 sq. ft.

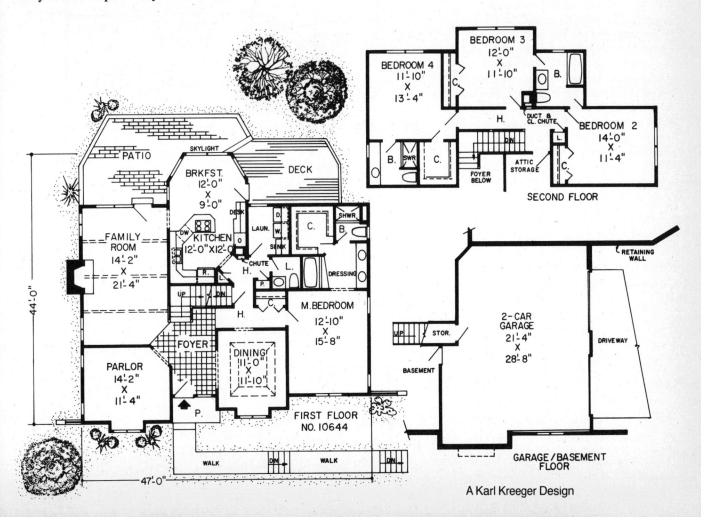

A Karl Kreeger Design

Build this House in a Beautiful Spot

No. 90672

This family home combines the charm of an early American Saltbox with contemporary drama. With a rear wall that's almost entirely glass and soaring ceilings pierced by skylights, active areas on the first floor unite with a full-length deck and back yard for an incredible outdoor feeling. But, beauty doesn't mean convenience has to be compromised. Look at the efficient galley kitchen, the adjoining pantry right by the rear entry, and the first-floor master bedroom served by a full bath. Survey the living areas below from the second floor balcony that opens to two bedrooms and another full bath.

First floor — 1,042 sq. ft.
Second floor — 519 sq. ft.
Mud/laundry room — 58 sq. ft.
Basement — 1,000 sq. ft.
Garage — 234 sq. ft.

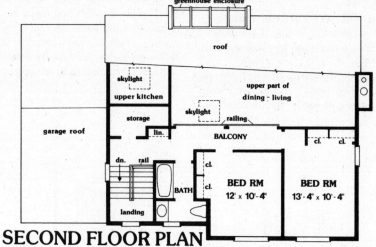

SECOND FLOOR PLAN

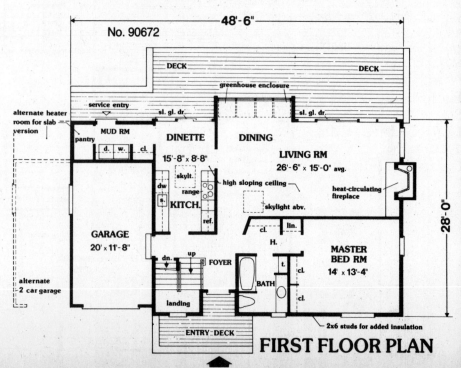

FIRST FLOOR PLAN

Skylights and Oversized Windows Brighten Every Room

No. 91244

A classic columned portico and solid brick facade put a traditional face on this distinctive plan. Inside, a sunny atmosphere and step-saving amenities throughout make this a house you'll love to live in. Look at the handy wetbar in the sloping living room, and the powder room for the convenience of your guests. Notice the ingenious arrangement of the skylit island kitchen and dining room — so close, yet separated by double doors when you want privacy. And, the adjacent wooden deck has a twin off the master suite, a pleasant retreat with a skylit bath and desirable first-floor location. Another skylight illuminates the vaulted media balcony which links the upstairs bedrooms and commands a bird's eye view of the living room.

First floor — 1,483 sq. ft.
Second floor — 882 sq. ft.
Unfinished basement — 1,439 sq. ft.
Garage — 429 sq. ft.

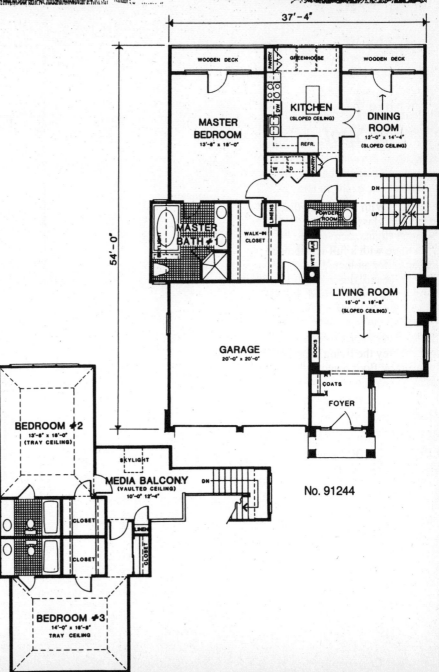

No. 91244

Colonial Charmer Fit for a Crowd

No. 20101

Imagine entertaining in this spacious masterpiece! Throw open the double doors between the front parlor and fire-placed family room and you've got an expansive room that can handle any crowd. There's room for an army of cooks in the bayed kitchen-breakfast room combination. And, when the oven overheats the room, head out to the adjoining deck for a breath of fresh air. Store extra supplies in the room-sized pantry on the way to the elegant, formal dining room. The adjacent breezeway contains a handy powder room and laundry facilities. Four bedrooms are tucked upstairs, away from the action. Look at the magnificent master suite. Recessed ceilings, a skylit shower, and double vanities make this room both luxurious and convenient.

First floor — 1,109 sq. ft.
Second floor — 932 sq. ft.
Basement — 1,109 sq. ft.
Garage — 552 sq. ft.

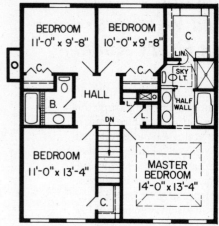

BEDROOM 11'-0" x 9'-8"
BEDROOM 10'-0" x 9'-8"
C.
LIN.
SKY LT.
HALL
C.
HALF WALL
B.
DN
BEDROOM 11'-0" x 13'-4"
MASTER BEDROOM 14'-0" x 13'-4"
C.

SECOND FLOOR

A Karl Kreeger Design

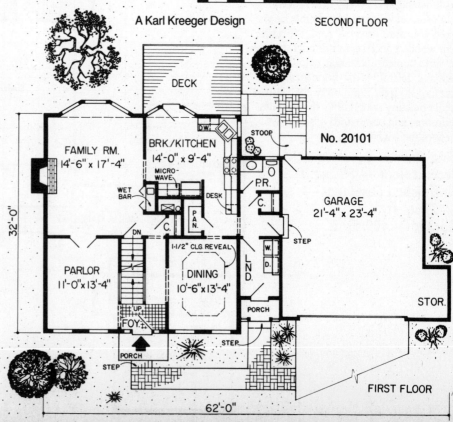

DECK

FAMILY RM. 14'-6" x 17'-4"

BRK./KITCHEN 14'-0" x 9'-4"

MICRO-WAVE

STOOP

No. 20101

WET BAR

DESK

P.R.

C.

GARAGE 21'-4" x 23'-4"

PAN.

DN

C.

STEP

1-1/2" CLG. REVEAL

W. D.

LND.

STEP

PARLOR 11'-0" x 13'-4"

DINING 10'-6" x 13'-4"

PORCH

STOR.

UP

FOY.

PORCH

STEP

STEP

32'-0"

62'-0"

FIRST FLOOR

Sun Space Warms To Entertaining

No. 10495

Tile is used to soak up solar heat in the sun space and also to add a tailored accent to the total home arrangement. Leading from the air-lock entry torward the living room spaces of this marvelous home, the tile separates the activity areas from the sleeping quarters. With two bedrooms on the second story, the lower area includes the master bedroom suite with its divided bath and walk-in closet. The utilitarian areas of the home are also enhanced by direct access to the sun space plus a space-stretching central island.

First floor — 1,691 sq. ft.
Second floor — 512 sq. ft.
Garage — 484 sq. ft.
Sun space — 108 sq. ft.
Basement — 1,691 sq. ft.

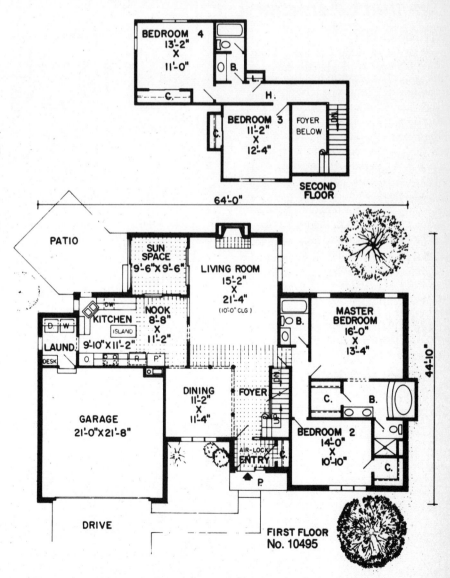

Elegant and Inviting

No. 10689

Traditional and modern elements unite to create an outstanding plan for the family that enjoys outdoor entertaining. Wrap-around verandas and a three-season porch insure the party will stay dry, rain or shine. You may want to keep guests inside, in the elegant parlor and formal dining room, separated by a half wall. The adjoining kitchen can be closed off to keep meal preparation convenient, but removed from the bustle. The family will enjoy informal meals at the island bar, or in the adjoining breakfast nook. Even the fireplaced gathering room, with its soaring ceilings and access to the porch, is right nearby. You'll appreciate the first-floor master suite, and the upstairs laundry location.

First floor — 1,580 sq. ft.
Second floor — 1,164 sq. ft.
Basement — 1,329 sq. ft.
Garage — 576 sq. ft.

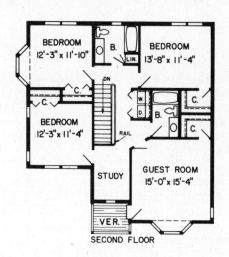

A Design by William E. Gage

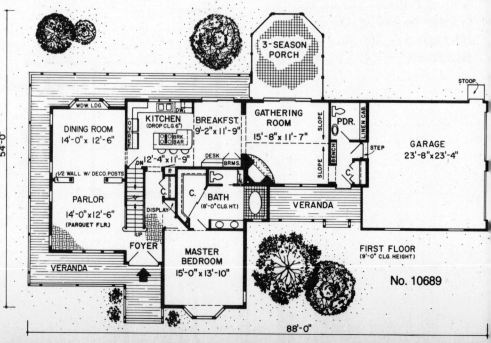

Four-bedroom Design Combines Multiple Features

No. 10522

All four bedrooms, including the well appointed master suite, are located on the second floor of this tastefully simple home. The first floor living areas are well zoned into formal and informal areas. The living room features a traditional picture window, a built-in bookcase and a fireplace. The dining room opens onto the deck through French doors and is located conveniently near the U-shaped kitchen. Additional first floor features include a guest bath, a laundry room and a sunny dining nook.

First floor — 873 sq. ft.
Second floor — 844 sq. ft.
Basement — 873 sq. ft.
Garage — 544 sq. ft.

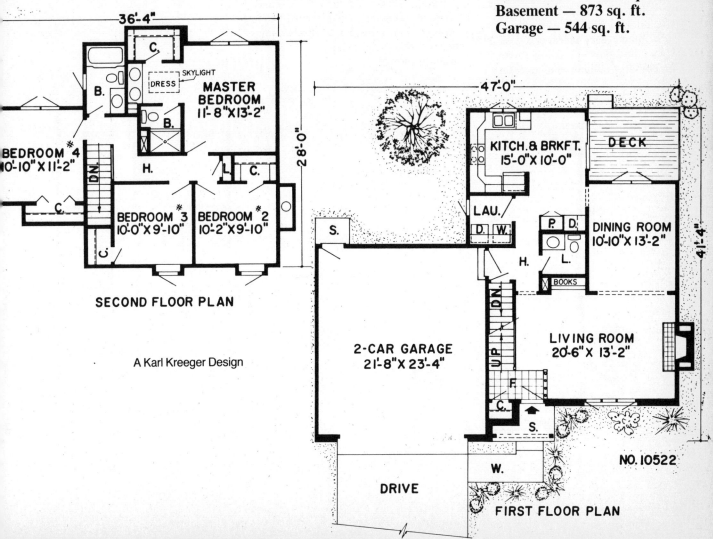

SECOND FLOOR PLAN

A Karl Kreeger Design

FIRST FLOOR PLAN

NO. 10522

Stacked Windows Create Exciting Exterior

No. 20009

Here's a three-bedroom beauty that unites interior living spaces with the great outdoors. A generous supply of huge windows, easy access to a deck and patio off the dining and family rooms, and a plan that eliminates unnecessary walls all add up to a wide-open atmosphere you'll love. The kitchen features a convenient pass-through to the sunny breakfast bay. And, thanks to the open plan, the cook can enjoy the cozy warmth of the family room fireplace. Upstairs, the two rear bedrooms share a full bath with double vanities. The master suite, dominated by a stacked window arrangement, features cathedral ceilings and a private bath with a raised tub and walk-in shower.

First floor — 982 sq. ft.
Second floor — 815 sq. ft.
Basement — 978 sq. ft.

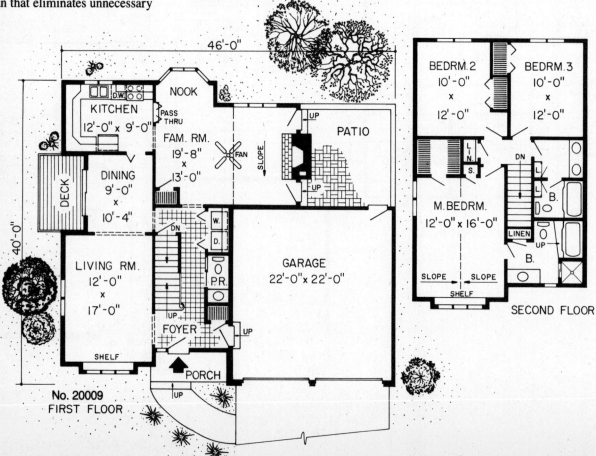

No. 20009
FIRST FLOOR

SECOND FLOOR

Design Combines Laundry, Bath

No. 10268

A large, closeted laundry and half bath combination show the emphasis on space and function in this attractive two story. The living room extends 20 feet to feature a fireplace, and the dining room opens to the patio via sliding glass doors. Zoned for sleeping, the upstairs groups three sizable bedrooms and two full baths, adding plentiful closet space.

First floor — 882 sq. ft.
Second floor — 875 sq. ft.
Covered patio — 600 sq. ft.
Garage — 576 sq. ft.
Basement — 882 sq. ft.

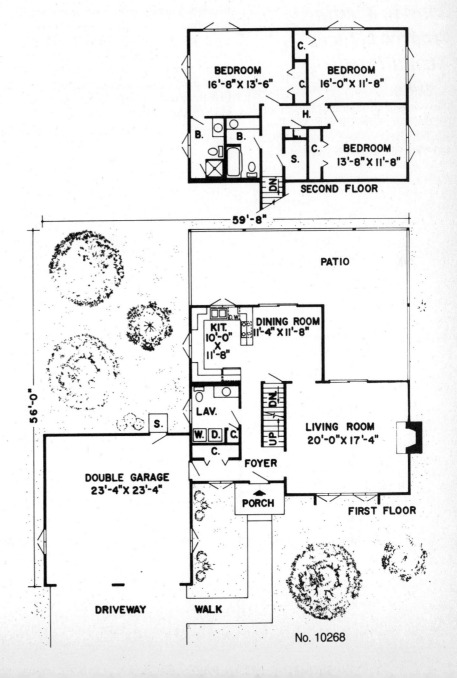

No. 10268

Floor-to-Ceiling Window Graces Formal Parlor

No. 20080

There's a taste of tudor elegance in this three-bedroom family home. You'll see it in the brick and stucco facade with rustic wood trim, in the tiled foyer, and in the fireplaced family room with ten foot ceilings. But, it's easy to see how convenient this plan is, too. The island kitchen and breakfast nook are adjacent to a gracious formal dining room and outdoor deck, perfect for a summer supper. The first-floor master suite means you won't have to trek down the stairs for your morning coffee. The kids will love their upstairs bath. A skylight assures privacy and a sunny atmosphere.

First floor — 1,859 sq. ft.
Second floor — 556 sq. ft.
Basement — 1,844 sq. ft.
Garage — 598 sq. ft.

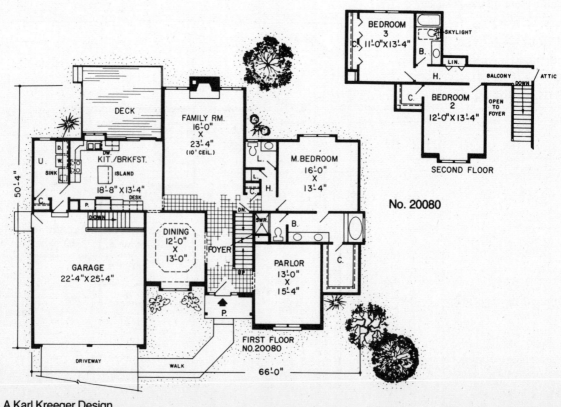

No. 20080

A Karl Kreeger Design

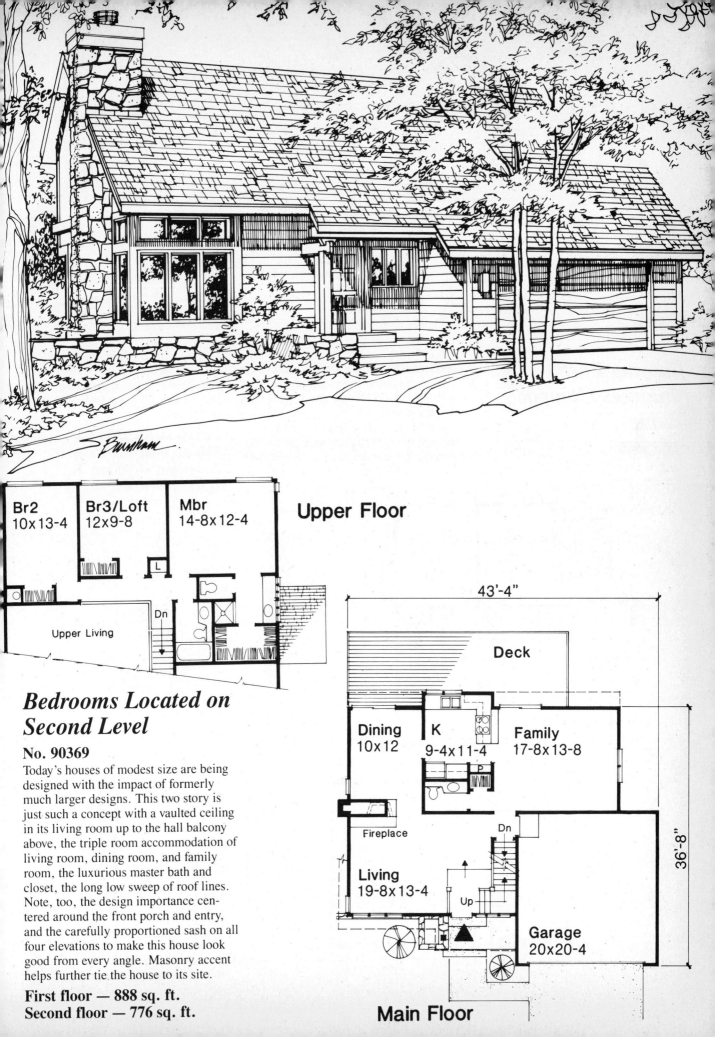

Upper Floor

Br2
10x13-4

Br3/Loft
12x9-8

Mbr
14-8x12-4

L

Dn

Upper Living

Bedrooms Located on Second Level

No. 90369

Today's houses of modest size are being designed with the impact of formerly much larger designs. This two story is just such a concept with a vaulted ceiling in its living room up to the hall balcony above, the triple room accommodation of living room, dining room, and family room, the luxurious master bath and closet, the long low sweep of roof lines. Note, too, the design importance centered around the front porch and entry, and the carefully proportioned sash on all four elevations to make this house look good from every angle. Masonry accent helps further tie the house to its site.

First floor — 888 sq. ft.
Second floor — 776 sq. ft.

43'-4"

Deck

Dining
10x12

K
9-4x11-4

Family
17-8x13-8

P

Fireplace

36'-8"

Dn

Living
19-8x13-4

Up

Garage
20x20-4

Main Floor

Inviting Porch Enlarges Compact Home

No. 10646

This modified cape with attached two car garage can house a growing family for a bargain price. Double doors in the cozy living room open to the bay-windowed family room with fireplace and patio access. Eat in the family-size kitchen or formal dining room. Up the central stairway, the vaulted ceiling in the master suite creates a spacious feeling. Three other bedrooms and a bath share the second floor.

First floor — 930 sq. ft.
Second floor — 980 sq. ft
Basement — 900 sq. ft.
Garage — 484 sq. ft.

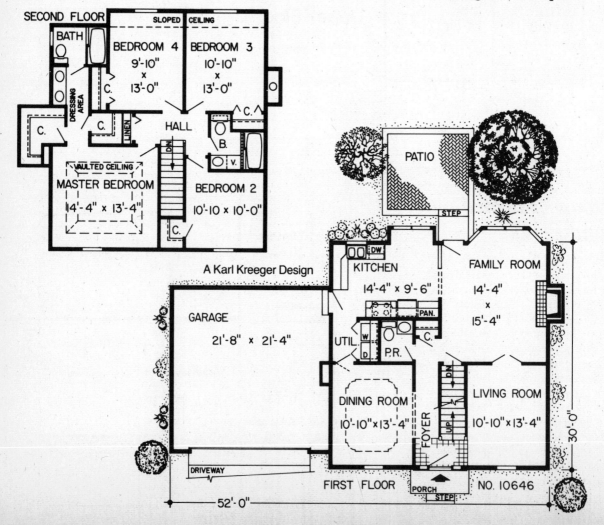

A Karl Kreeger Design

Classic and Comfortable

No. 90435

A central staircase dominates the spacious foyer of this efficient Tudor home. The convenient, L-shaped arrangement of kitchen, formal, and informal dining rooms means meal service will be a breeze. And, the elegance of a massive fireplace, French doors, and an adjoining rear deck make the great room a special spot. With three bedrooms and two full baths, there's room for the whole family upstairs. Use the bayed study off the master suite as a nursery, or a quiet getaway for those rare moments when you have time to relax.

First floor — 1,032 sq. ft.
Second floor — 1,050 sq. ft.

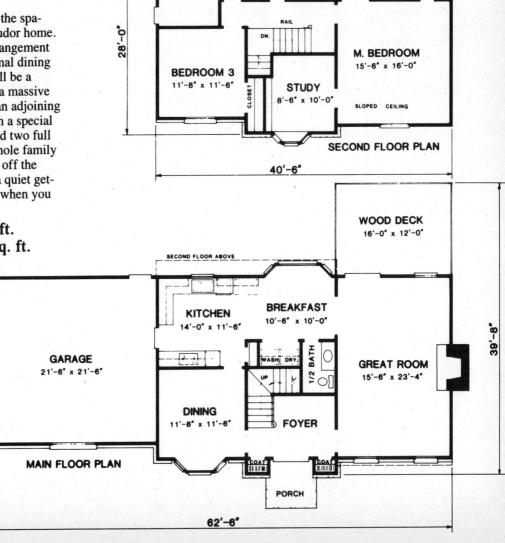

Glass Captures Views & Sun

No. 90121

Abundant glass floods this plan with light and offers images of the surrounding scenery from three sides, as well as serving as a solar energy feature. Large exterior exposed beams crisscross the glass giving a massive, rugged appearance. The center of family activity begins in the family room and proceeds to the deck which flows into a dining patio on the left side. Your family may relax over meals here or in the dining/kitchen area just inside glass doors. Two bedrooms, a full bath and laundry facilities complete the first level. An open wooden stairway beckons you to the second level which opens into a large fireplaced sitting room and balcony overlooking the family room.

First floor — 1,126 sq. ft.
Second floor — 603 sq. ft.

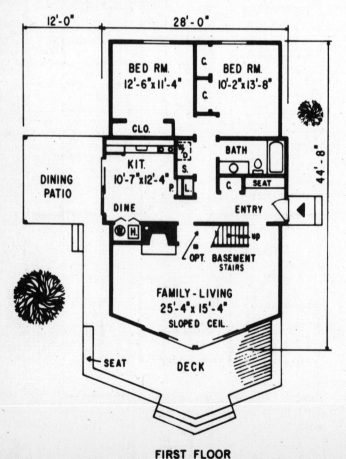

FIRST FLOOR

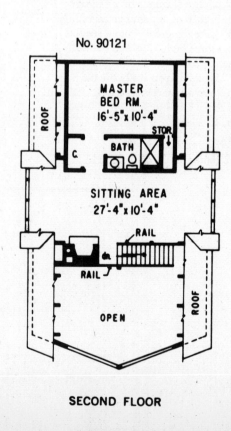

SECOND FLOOR

94

Designed for Privacy

No. 10657

From the three car garage to the sunroom with hot tub, this house is equipped for gracious living. The skylit foyer leads three ways: up to 2 bedrooms, a full bath, and dramatic loft with balcony; into the formal dining room with bump out window and recessed ceiling; or into the ample living room, flooded with light and featuring a fireplace. The island kitchen is convenient to both living and morning rooms. Approach the deck or sunroom from the morning room. The master bedroom suite, which features a room-sized closet, double vanity, and skylit tub with separate shower, is tucked away into its own corner for maximum privacy.

First floor — 1,831 sq. ft.
Second floor — 814 sq. ft.
Basement — 1,831 sq. ft.
Garage — 828 sq. ft.

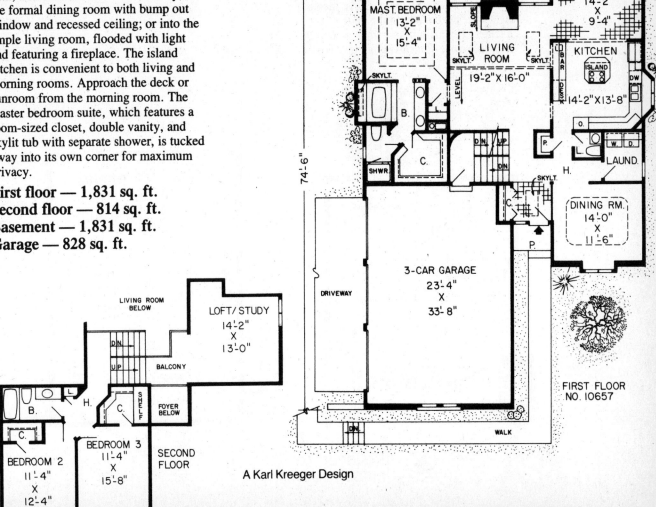

A Karl Kreeger Design

Mountain Retreat

No. 10751

Relax and enjoy this compact vacation home. With vertical cedar siding, you won't need to expend much energy on exterior upkeep. The central entry opens right into the living room, a warm and spacious center of activity. Serve meals right over the counter in the galley kitchen. The main floor bedroom and full bath make one-floor living an inviting option. Save the stairs for the guests, unless you want to take advantage of the view from the balcony!

First floor — 660 sq. ft.
Second floor — 330 sq. ft.

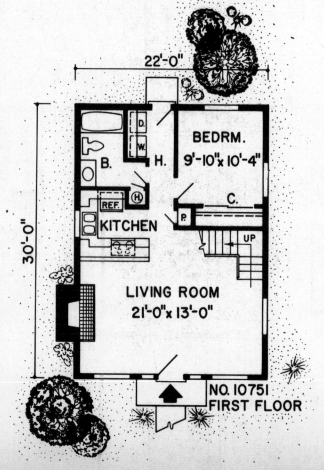

22'-0"
30'-0"

B.
D.
W.
H.
BEDRM.
9'-10"x 10'-4"
REF.
KITCHEN
C.
P.
UP

LIVING ROOM
21'-0"x 13'-0"

NO. 10751
FIRST FLOOR

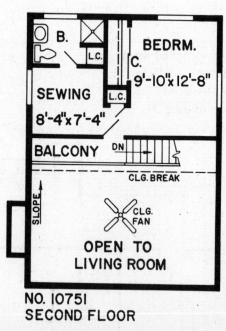

B.
L.C.
BEDRM.
9'-10"x 12'-8"
SEWING
8'-4"x 7'-4"
L.C.
BALCONY
DN
SLOPE
CLG. BREAK
CLG. FAN
OPEN TO
LIVING ROOM

NO. 10751
SECOND FLOOR

No. 10751

Balcony Affords Splendid View

No. 20097

Standing in the central foyer, you can see active areas and the rear deck off this sunny classic in one glance. Straight ahead, the living room ceiling, pierced by a skylight, soars to a two-story height. Living and dining rooms flow together in one spacious unit. And, both are easily served by the handy kitchen with a breakfast bar peninsula. Down a hallway off the living room, you'll find a quiet sleeping wing behind the garage. Two bedrooms feature access to an adjoining bath with double vanities. The second floor is all yours. Imagine stealing away for a luxurious soak in your private tub, or a relaxing afternoon with your favorite book.

First floor — 1,752 sq. ft.
Second floor — 897 sq. ft.
Basement — 1,752 sq. ft.
Garage — 531 sq. ft.

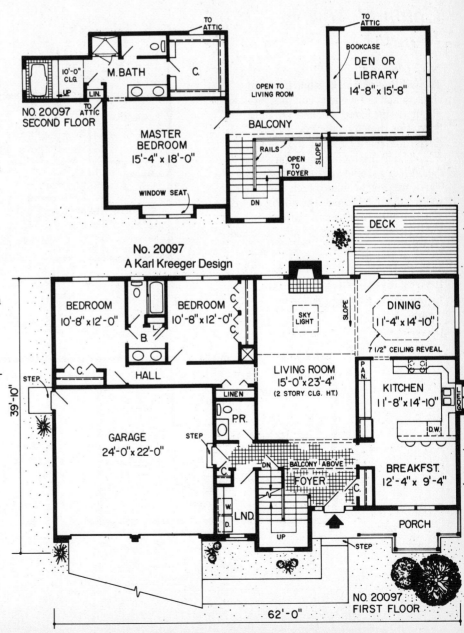

Colonial Always Popular

No. 148

The old English brick, white louvered shutters and tall wooden columns provide dignity to the exterior. There are three bedrooms shown on the lower level. Each room has a closet of above average size. The living room is quite large and can utilize a scenic view from both ends. The lower level contains both family room and hobby room. The hobby room can also serve as an extra bedroom or guest room. The garage is extra large and provides storage space.

Upper level — 1,140 sq. ft.
Lower level — 1,140 sq. ft.
Garage — 644 sq. ft.

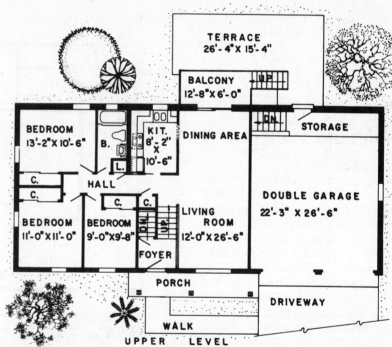

TERRACE 26'-4" X 15'-4"

BALCONY 12'-8" X 6'-0"

STORAGE

BEDROOM 13'-2" X 10'-6"

B.

KIT. 8'-2" X 10'-6"

DINING AREA

DN

DOUBLE GARAGE 22'-3" X 26'-6"

C.

C.

HALL

BEDROOM 11'-0" X 11'-0"

BEDROOM 9'-0" X 9'-8"

C.

C.

DN

LIVING ROOM 12'-0" X 26'-6"

FOYER

PORCH

DRIVEWAY

WALK

UPPER LEVEL

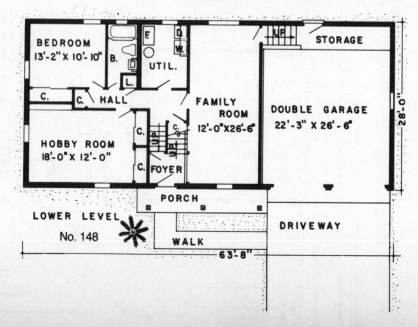

BEDROOM 13'-2" X 10'-10"

B.

UTIL.

STORAGE

C.

C.

HALL

FAMILY ROOM 12'-0" X 26'-6"

DOUBLE GARAGE 22'-3" X 26'-6"

28'-0"

HOBBY ROOM 18'-0" X 12'-0"

C.

C.

C.

FOYER

PORCH

DRIVEWAY

LOWER LEVEL
No. 148

WALK

63'-8"

Family Activities Plus Elegant Style

No. 90100

Two garden patios, one off the kitchen and one off the great room, increase the elegant living available in this spacious home. The great room's cathedral ceiling opens onto the loft above and creates an expansive atmosphere which is complemented by the stone fireplace. Two bedrooms across the front of the house might also be used as a den or library or turned to other functional use. The master bedroom's bath is designed for privacy but may also be shared with one of the front bedrooms.

First floor — 1,898 sq. ft.
Second floor — 400 sq. ft.

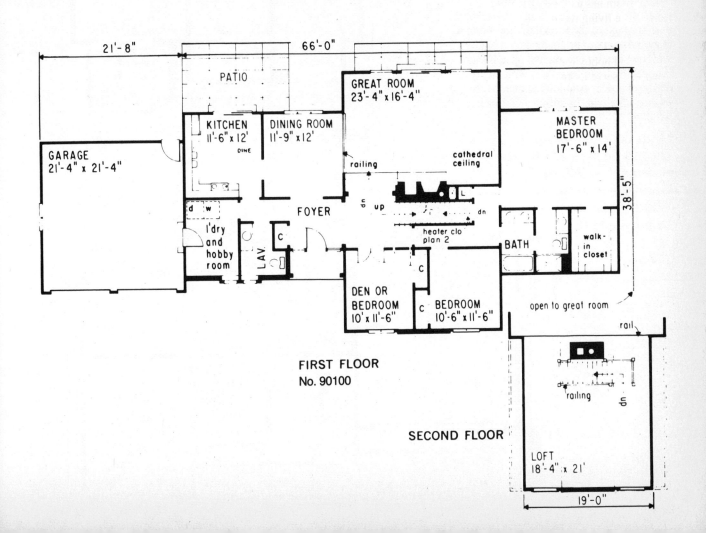

GARAGE
21'-4" x 21'-4"

PATIO

KITCHEN
11'-6" x 12'

DINING ROOM
11'-9" x 12'

GREAT ROOM
23'-4" x 16'-4"

MASTER BEDROOM
17'-6" x 14'

cathedral ceiling

railing

FOYER

l'dry and hobby room

LAV.

heater clo plan 2

BATH

walk-in closet

DEN OR BEDROOM
10' x 11'-6"

BEDROOM
10'-6" x 11'-6"

open to great room

21'-8"   66'-0"

38'-5"

FIRST FLOOR
No. 90100

rail

railing

SECOND FLOOR

LOFT
18'-4" x 21'

19'-0"

Great Traffic Pattern Highlights Home

No. 90901

Victorian styling and economical construction techniques make this a doubly charming design. This is a compact charmer brimming with features: a sheltered entry leading to the two-story foyer; an island kitchen with convenient pass-through to the formal dining room; a cozy living room brightened by a bay window; an airy central hall upstairs surrounded by large bedrooms with plenty of closet space. And look at that lovely master suite with its sitting area in a bay window.

Main floor — 940 sq. ft.
Second floor — 823 sq. ft.
Basement — 940 sq. ft.
Garage — 440 sq. ft.
Width — 54 ft.
Depth — 33 ft.

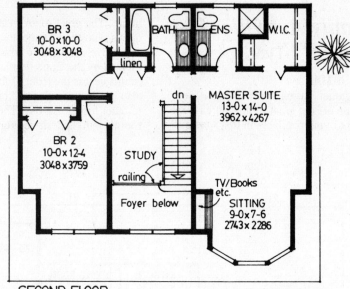

SECOND FLOOR   No. 90901

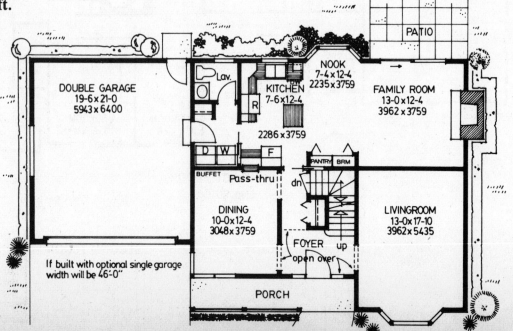

Porch Adorns Elegant Bay

No. 20093

Here's a compact Victorian charmer that unites tradition with today in a perfect combination. Imagine waking up in the roomy master suite with its romantic bay and full bath with double sinks. Two additional bedrooms, which feature huge closets, share the hall bath. The romance continues in the sunny breakfast room off the island kitchen, in the recessed ceilings of the formal dining room, and in the living room's cozy fireplace. Sun lovers will appreciate the sloping, skylit ceilings in the living room, and the rear deck accessible from both the kitchen and living room.

First floor — 978 sq. ft.
Second floor — 812 sq. ft.
Basement — 978 sq. ft.

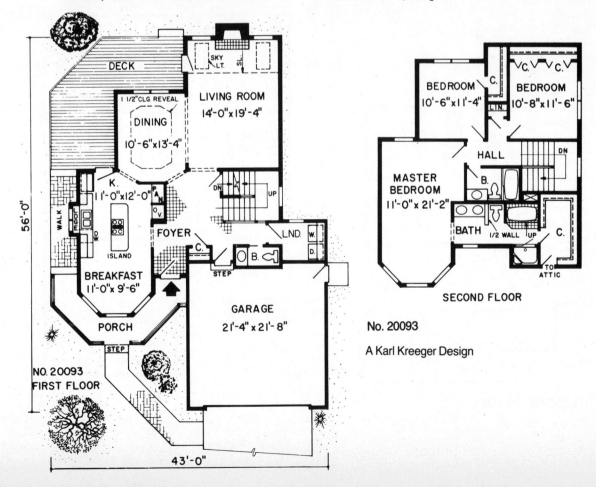

No. 20093

A Karl Kreeger Design

Contemporary Exterior

No. 90327

A spacious feeling is created by the ingenious arrangement of the living areas of this comfortable home. The inviting living room offers a cozy fireplace, a front corner full of windows, a vaulted ceiling and an open staircase. The clerestory windows further accent the open design of the dining room and kitchen. The U-shaped kithen welcomes cook and tasters alike with its open preparation areas. Secluded from the rest of the main floor and the other two bedrooms, the master bedroom features a walk-in closet and a large, compartmented bath which may also serve as a guest bathroom. Two additional bedrooms and a full bath comprise the upper floor.

Main floor — 846 sq. ft.
Upper floor — 400 sq. ft.
Basement — 846 sq. ft.
Garage — 400 sq. ft.

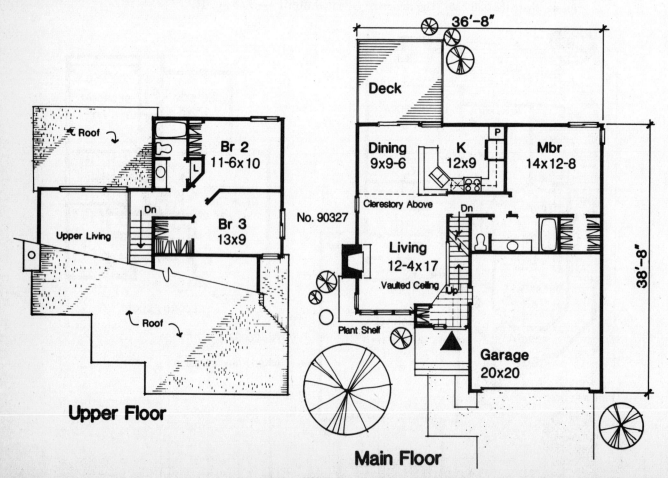

Upper Floor

Main Floor

Updated Traditional Flooded with Sunlight

No. 20305

Elegance and convenience combine in this one-of-a-kind family home. From triple half-round windows to the shaded entry, the clapboard exterior only hints at the beauty inside. Barrel-vaults, sloping ceilings, and an angular plan give every room a distinctive shape. And, the handy arrangement of the eat-in kitchen, formal dining room, and family room pass through makes mealtime a simple matter. A wall of glass doors unites the living and family rooms with a full-length deck at the rear of the house, affording a panoramic view of the back yard. Upstairs, skylights cast a sunny glow on the three bedrooms and two full baths.

First floor — 1,095 sq. ft.
Second floor — 725 sq. ft.
Basement — 1,025 sq. ft.
Garage — 400 sq. ft.

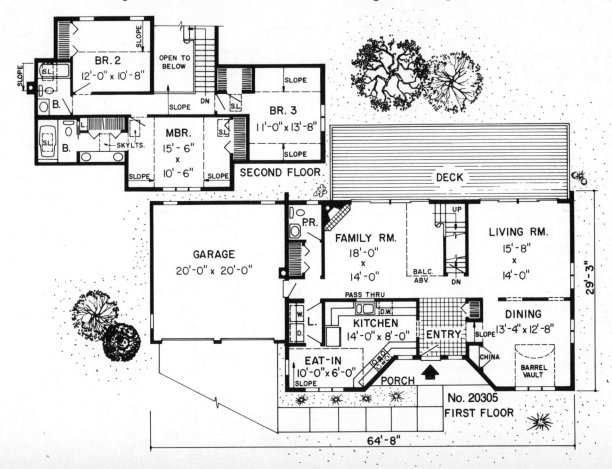

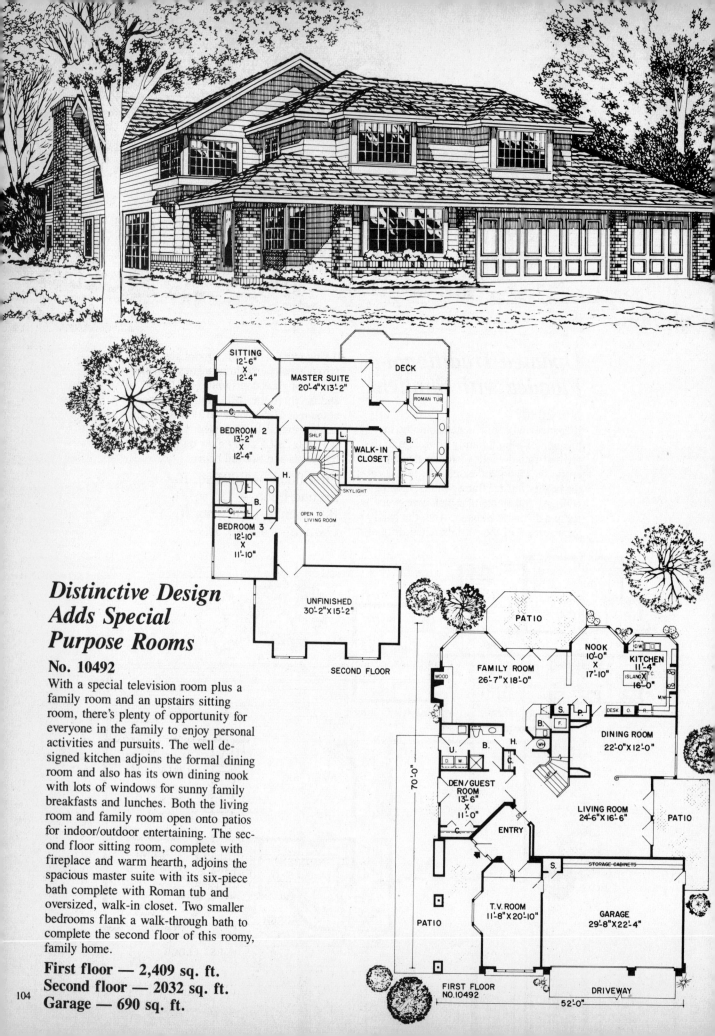

Distinctive Design Adds Special Purpose Rooms

No. 10492

With a special television room plus a family room and an upstairs sitting room, there's plenty of opportunity for everyone in the family to enjoy personal activities and pursuits. The well designed kitchen adjoins the formal dining room and also has its own dining nook with lots of windows for sunny family breakfasts and lunches. Both the living room and family room open onto patios for indoor/outdoor entertaining. The second floor sitting room, complete with fireplace and warm hearth, adjoins the spacious master suite with its six-piece bath complete with Roman tub and oversized, walk-in closet. Two smaller bedrooms flank a walk-through bath to complete the second floor of this roomy, family home.

First floor — 2,409 sq. ft.
Second floor — 2032 sq. ft.
Garage — 690 sq. ft.

SECOND FLOOR

- SITTING 12'-6" X 12'-4"
- MASTER SUITE 20'-4" X 13'-2"
- DECK
- ROMAN TUB
- BEDROOM 2 13'-2" X 12'-4"
- WALK-IN CLOSET
- SKYLIGHT
- OPEN TO LIVING ROOM
- BEDROOM 3 12'-10" X 11'-10"
- UNFINISHED 30'-2" X 15'-2"

FIRST FLOOR NO. 10492

- PATIO
- FAMILY ROOM 26'-7" X 18'-0"
- NOOK 10'-0" X 17'-10"
- KITCHEN 11'-4"
- ISLAND 16'-0"
- DINING ROOM 22'-0" X 12'-0"
- DEN/GUEST ROOM 13'-6" X 11'-0"
- ENTRY
- LIVING ROOM 24'-6" X 16'-6"
- PATIO
- STORAGE CABINETS
- T.V. ROOM 11'-8" X 20'-10"
- GARAGE 29'-8" X 22'-4"
- PATIO
- DRIVEWAY
- 70'-0"
- 52'-0"

Distinctive Plan Boasts Lofty Living Room

No. 91303

You can have both convenience and privacy in this dramatic contemporary with a first-floor master suite. Imagine how easy that early-morning walk to the coffee pot will be, with the kitchen just across the hall. And, with the sunken, formal dining room, fireplaced family room, and breakfast bay right next door to the kitchen, mealtimes will be a breeze, too. The cozy den, tucked in a private spot behind the garage, could double as a guest room or home office. Intriguing nooks and crannies will present endless decorating possibilities in the living room up the stairway off the entry. Step up another flight to the loft that leads to two more bedrooms and a full bath.

Main level — 1,730 sq. ft.
Upper level — 570 sq. ft.

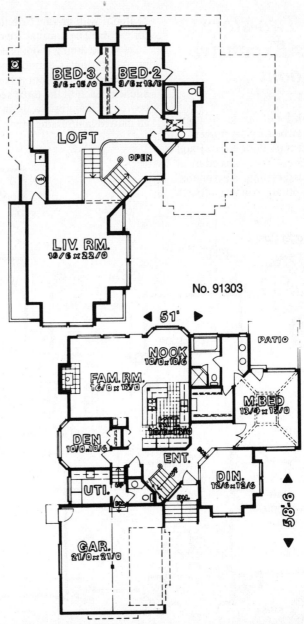

No. 91303

Elegant Two-story Features Expansive Great Room

No. 10526

The central corridor of this lovely home features both a two-story foyer overlooked by the second floor balcony and the expansive Great Room graced by a beamed, cathedral ceiling. Also on the first floor are a library-den and a fourth bedroom with private bath that is ideal for guests. The unusual window treatment in the dining room is echoed in the breakfast room. Centrally located between these two rooms is the spacious kitchen. Each of the three second floor bedrooms features a walk-in closet and an individual dressing area.

First floor — 1,890 sq. ft.
Second floor — 1,399 sq. ft.
Basement — 1,890 sq. ft.
Garage — 529 sq. ft.

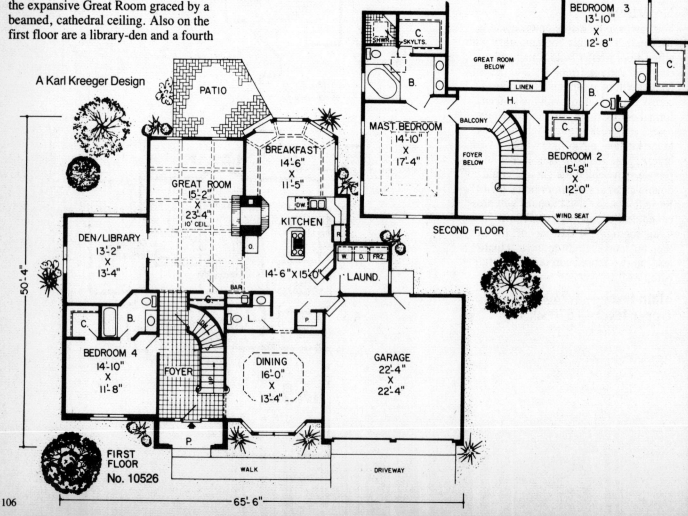

A Karl Kreeger Design

PATIO

BREAKFAST 14'-6" X 11'-5"

GREAT ROOM 15'-2" X 23'-4" 10' CEIL.

DW

KITCHEN 14'-6" X 15'-0"

DEN/LIBRARY 13'-2" X 13'-4"

BAR

LAUND. W. D. FRZ

BEDROOM 4 14'-10" X 11'-8"

C. B.

FOYER

DINING 16'-0" X 13'-4"

GARAGE 22'-4" X 22'-4"

FIRST FLOOR No. 10526

WALK   DRIVEWAY

50'-4"

65'-6"

SHWR C. SKYLTS.

B.

MAST. BEDROOM 14'-10" X 17'-4"

BALCONY

FOYER BELOW

GREAT ROOM BELOW

LINEN

H.

BEDROOM 3 13'-10" X 12'-8"

C.

B.

C.

BEDROOM 2 15'-8" X 12'-0"

WIND. SEAT

SECOND FLOOR

Keeping Room Meets Living-dining Needs

No. 26830

A warm, homey atmosphere is created by the design of this cozy house. Its moderate square footage yields itself to ample room for many family purposes. Dormer windows look in on two bedrooms and a bath on the second level. A spacy keeping room with its own outside entrance and fireplace becomes the center of family dining and living on the lower level. The master bedroom, also with a fireplace and its own bath, is sepa- rated from the rest of the house by the kitchen area. An attractive covered porch serves both the garage and a small foyer.

First floor — 1,026 sq. ft.
Second floor — 520 sq. ft.
Basement — 1,026 sq. ft.
Garage — 308 sq. ft.

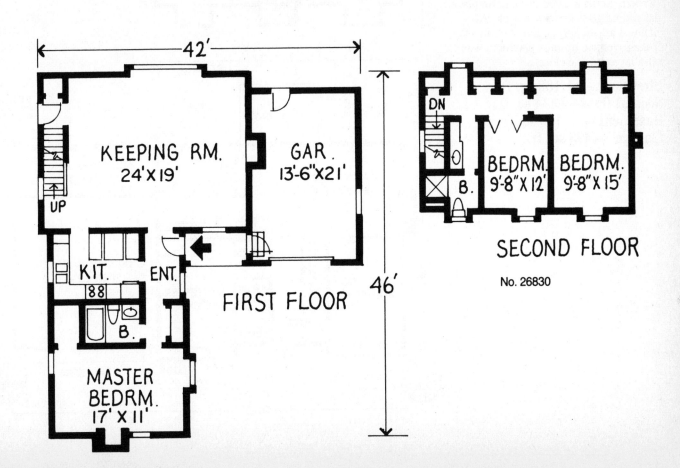

KEEPING RM. 24' X 19'

GAR. 13-6"X21'

UP

KIT.

ENT.

B.

MASTER BEDRM. 17' X 11'

FIRST FLOOR

42'

46'

DN

BEDRM. 9-8" X 12'

BEDRM. 9-8" X 15'

B.

SECOND FLOOR

No. 26830

Triple Dormers Distinguish Plan

No. 10354

Dormers extend the upstairs bedrooms and bath and add interest to the facade of this two level design. Traditional charm pervades the interior as well, with the kitchen opening to a 21-ft. screened porch, ideal for dining or napping. The first floor master bedroom shows double closets and adjoins a full bath. The family room merits a wood-burning fireplace and sliding glass doors to a deck. Also included are the formal living room left of the foyer and upstairs playroom with extra large storage closets.

First floor — 1,188 sq. ft.
Second floor — 834 sq. ft.
Basement — 1,140 sq. ft.
Garage — 498 sq. ft.

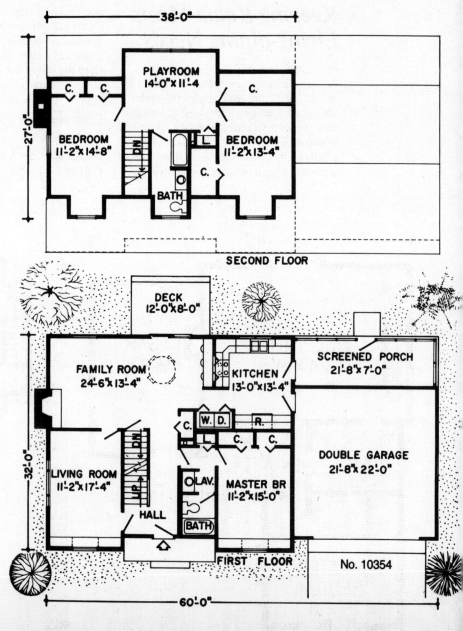

Elegant Home Provides Formal And Informal Areas

No. 10532

The elegant courtyard entry sets the tone for this home's blend of informal living highlighted by formal accents. A library and formal dining room are complemented by an open great room, large family-style kitchen and dining nook. Outdoor areas include a sun porch, a covered porch and a patio. The fully appointed master bedroom features individual dressing areas with his and her walk-in closets, plus a large bath with tub and shower. The second floor is comprised of three bedrooms and two more baths all linked by a balcony which overlooks the two-story foyer.

First floor—2,618 sq. ft.
Second floor—1,195 sq. ft.
Basement—2,396 sq. ft.
Garage—559 sq. ft.

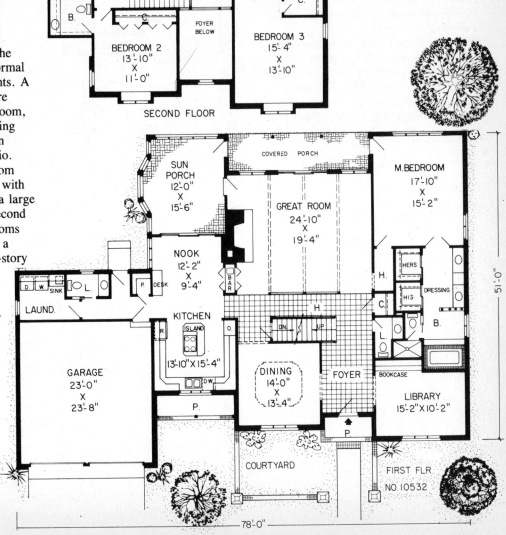

A Karl Kreeger Design

Graceful Elegance, Family-Style

No. 91020

A towering bay gives this beautiful home an impressive facade. Inside, the drama continues. Vaulted ceilings add a spacious airiness to the central entry, living, dining, and master bedrooms. You'll find a cheerful atmosphere throughout the house. Abundant windows and an open plan give the bayed family room, nook and kitchen a sunny warmth. Upstairs, the four bedrooms and two full baths include the luxurious master suite, dominated by a huge, half-round bay window.

Total living area — 2,157 sq. ft.

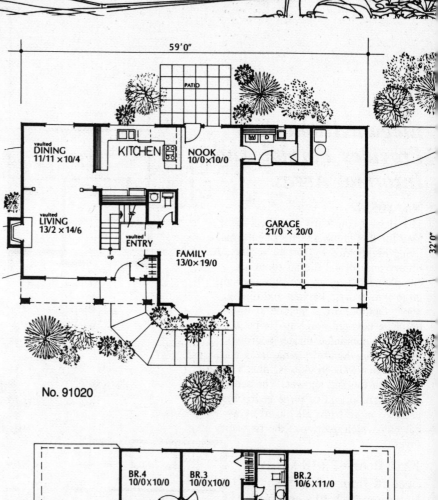

No. 91020

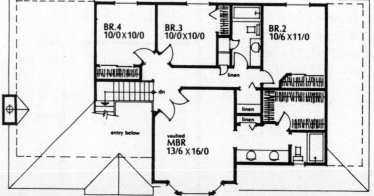

Entry Hints at Appealing Interior

No. 10678

Interesting angles give every room in this three-bedroom home a distinctive shape. Stand in the foyer and look up. Soaring ceilings in the window-walled living room rise to dizzying heights. Step past the powder room to find a fireplaced family room, wide open to the convenient kitchen with built-in desk and pantry. Just outside, there's lots of warm weather living space on the deck surrounding the dining room. Walk upstairs to the vaulted den that links the bedrooms and provides a comfortable spot for enjoying a good book. And, look at the adjoining deck! Can't you imagine perching up there on a sunny day, watching the world go by?

First floor — 1,375 sq. ft.
Second floor — 1,206 sq. ft.
Basement — 1,375 sq. ft.

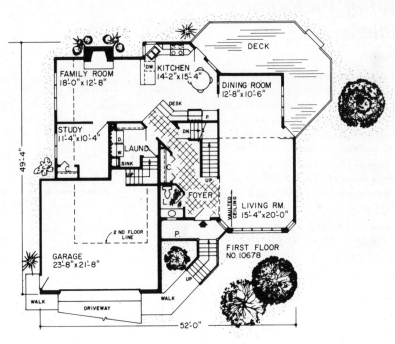

No. 10678   A Design by William E. Gage

A Hint of Victorian Nostalgia

No. 90909

High roofs, tower bays, and long, railed porches give this efficient plan an old-fashioned charm that's hard to resist. The foyer opens on a classic center stairwell, wrapped in short halls that separate traffic without subtracting from room sizes. The highlight of this home for many homeowners is sure to be the lively kitchen with its full bay window and built-in eating table.

Main floor — 1,206 sq. ft.
Second floor — 969 sq. ft.
Garage — 471 sq. ft.
Unfinished basement — 1,206 sq. ft.
Width — 61 ft.
Depth — 44 ft.

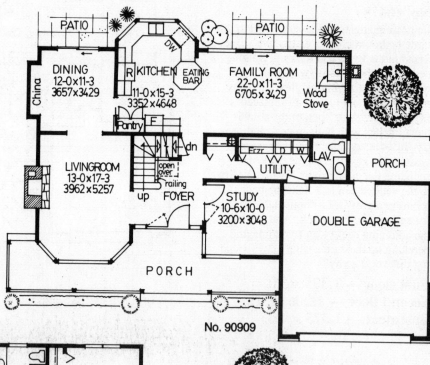

No. 90909

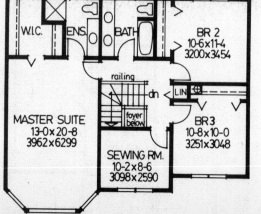

SECOND FLOOR

Bridge Forms Focal Point

No. 10419

Wrap around stairs and a bridge hold the central position for both location and interest in the floor plan. The bridge functions to connect the stairway with second floor bedrooms, crossing the open space created by the two story ceilings of the family room and entryway. Double hung windows cover both stories of the rear wall of the family room, looking out onto a patio on the lower level and deck on the second level.

First floor — 2,445 sq. ft.
Second floor — 898 sq. ft.
Garage — 687 sq. ft.
Covered Patios — 244 sq. ft.

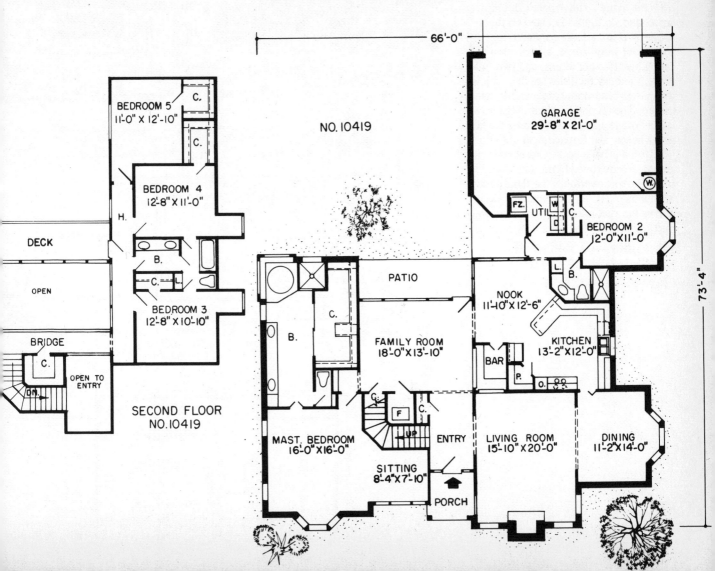

Studio Loft Offers Versatility

No. 10388

Sunwall water tubes and clay tile floors gather and store solar heat during the day from the many southern glass doors, windows, and skylights. Located on the lower level are a more formal living room with wood stove, kitchen area with eating bar, two bedrooms, and two full baths. Laundry facilities are tucked into the master beadroom bath area for convenience. The second level unfolds into a large storage area, which houses the hot water heater and furnace, and a studio loft with a private deck. Closet space is ample. Northern skylights add illumination. The loft overlooks the family room from a balcony. This openness of design allows for maximum air circulation and maximum use of the solar heat.

First floor — 1,248 sq. ft.
Studio loft — 357 sq. ft.
Garage — 640 sq. ft.

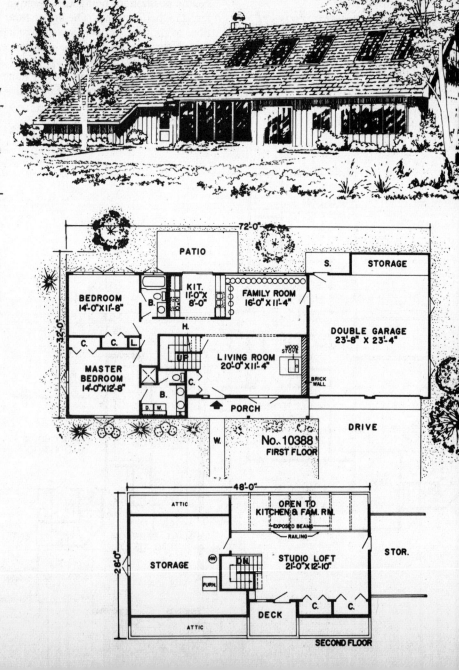

Stucco and Stone Reveal Outstanding Tudor Design

No. 10555

This beautiful stucco and stone masonry Tudor design opens to a formal foyer that leads through double doors into a well-designed library which is also conveniently accessible from the master bedroom. The master bedroom offers a vaulted ceiling and a huge bath area. Other features are an oversized living room with a fireplace, an open kitchen and a connecting dining room. A utility room and half bath are located next to a two-car garage. One other select option in this design is the separate cedar closet to use for off-season clothes storage.

First floor — 1,671 sq. ft.
Second floor — 505 sq. ft.
Basement — 1,661 sq. ft.
Garage — 604 sq. ft.
Screened porch — 114 sq. ft.

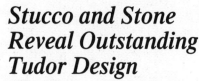

SECOND FLOOR

BEDROOM 11'-8" X 9'-10"

CEDAR CLOS.

C.

B.

DN.

BALCONY

FOYER BELOW

BEDROOM 11'-8" X 13'-2"

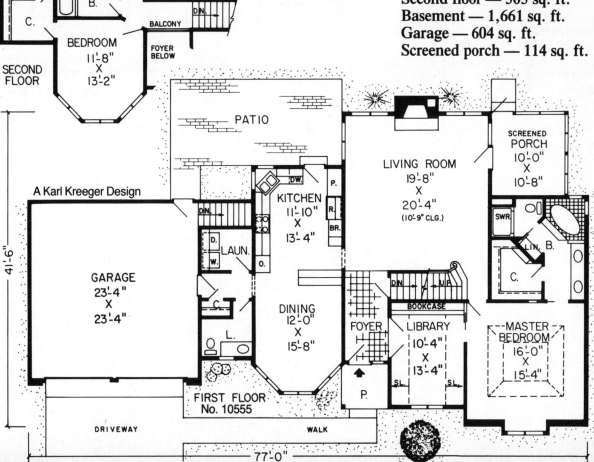

A Karl Kreeger Design

PATIO

KITCHEN 11'-10" X 13'-4"

LAUN.

GARAGE 23'-4" X 23'-4"

41'-6"

LIVING ROOM 19'-8" X 20'-4" (10'-9" CLG.)

SCREENED PORCH 10'-0" X 10'-8"

SWR

LIN. B.

C.

DINING 12'-0" X 15'-8"

FOYER

BOOKCASE

LIBRARY 10'-4" X 13'-4"

MASTER BEDROOM 16'-0" X 15'-4"

FIRST FLOOR No. 10555

P.

SL.

SL.

DRIVEWAY

WALK

77'-0"

Two-story Foyer Marks Fabulous Design

No. 90514

Enter a stunning 2-story foyer with tiled floor. Excellent traffic patterns provide discrete access to kitchen, linen and laundry facilities. The kitchen and breakfast nook boast easy dining and quick access to the deck through sliding doors. The sunken family and living rooms each have a cozy fireplace. The bedrooms are grouped on the 2nd floor, with a walk-in closet and dressing area for the master. Another prominent feature is the 3-car garage.

First floor — 1,599 sq. ft.
Second floor — 1,236 sq. ft.
Bonus room — 429 sq. ft.

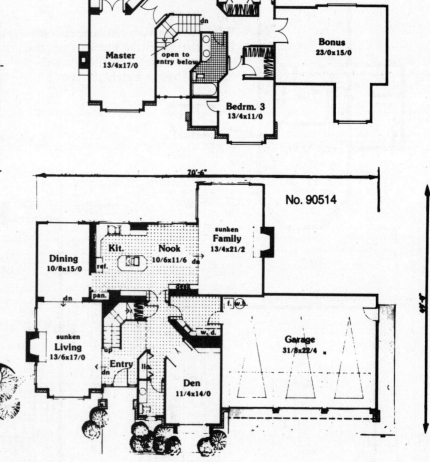

Contemporary Offers Sunken Living Room

No. 90334

This contemporary design is inviting because of the built-in greenhouse that is located just left of the entry into the house. Inside a sunken living room is accessible from the hallway. Once in the living room, you're greeted by a vaulted ceiling and a masonry fireplace. A formal dining room is located next to the living room. An efficient kitchen has a connecting breakfast room which appears larger because of its vaulted ceiling. An outside wooden deck is accessible from the kitchen/breakfast rooms. The family room has its own wood-burning fireplace and a wet bar. Laundry facilities are located near the family room. The second floor includes four bedrooms. The master bedroom has a his/hers walk-in closet, a whirlpool bath surrounded by tile and a cathedral ceiling with circle top windows.

First floor — 1,382 sq. ft.
Second floor — 1,328 sq. ft.

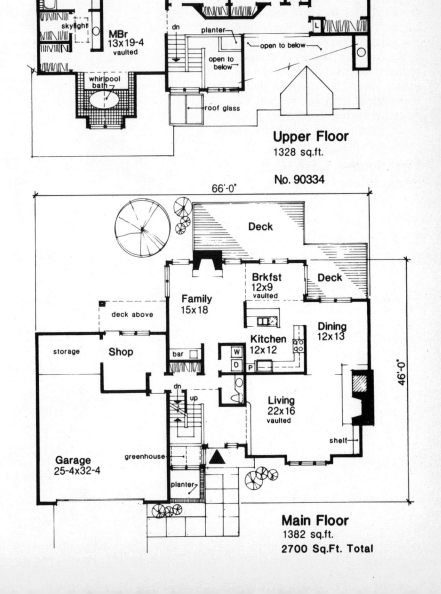

Upper Floor
1328 sq.ft.

No. 90334

Main Floor
1382 sq.ft.
2700 Sq.Ft. Total

Distinctive Styling with Vaulted Ceiling

No. 90516

Elegant lines are accented by french windows and brick facade on this stylish home. A sunken family room with fireplace and vaulted ceiling is overlooked by the 2nd floor balcony. The master bedroom has luxury touches like a sunken tub and large walk-in closet. Tile floors extend from the foyer into the oversized kitchen. Note the excellent traffic patterns to the dining area, family room, and deck.

First floor — 1,516 sq. ft.
Second floor — 1,153 sq. ft.

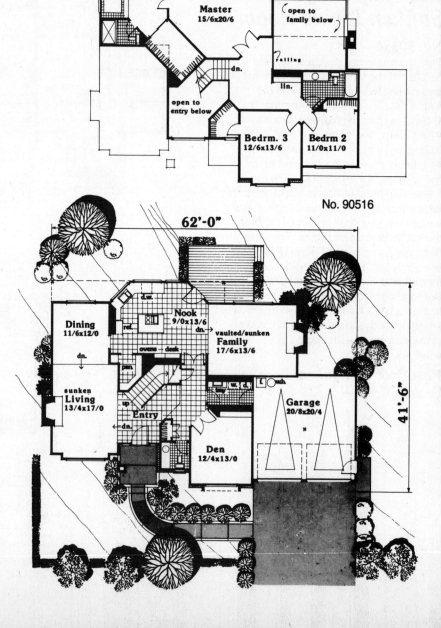

Modified A-Frame at Home Anywhere

No. 90309

Comfortable living in this compact plan is equally at home in suburbia or at a resort. The main floor includes a combined living/dining room whose ceiling reaches to the second floor loft. This living area is further enhanced by its view of the angled deck through corner windows and two sliding glass doors. Located at one end of the rear deck is a roomy outdoor storage cabinet. The galley-style kitchen is located near both the front entrance and the laundry area for convenience. Completing the main floor are a bedroom, full bath and note the fireplace with its large hearth. There is an optional bedroom and half-bath in addition to the loft on the second floor.

First floor — 735 sq. ft.
Second floor — 304 sq. ft.

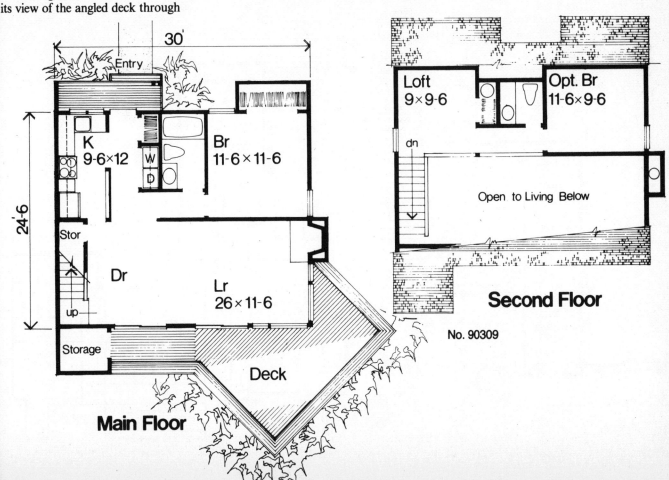

No. 90309

Main Floor

Second Floor

Arches Dominate Stately Facade

No. 10666

Gracious living is the rule in this brick masterpiece designed with an eye toward elegant entertaining. Window walls and French doors link the in-ground pool and surrounding brick patio with interior living spaces. The wetbar with wine storage provides a convenient space for a large buffet in the family room. Built-in bookcases in the living room, family room, and skylit second-floor library can house even the largest collection. Separated from living areas by halls or a bridge, every bedroom is a quiet retreat, with its own dressing room and adjoining bath.

First floor — 3,625 sq. ft.
Second floor — 937 sq. ft.
Garage — 636 sq. ft.

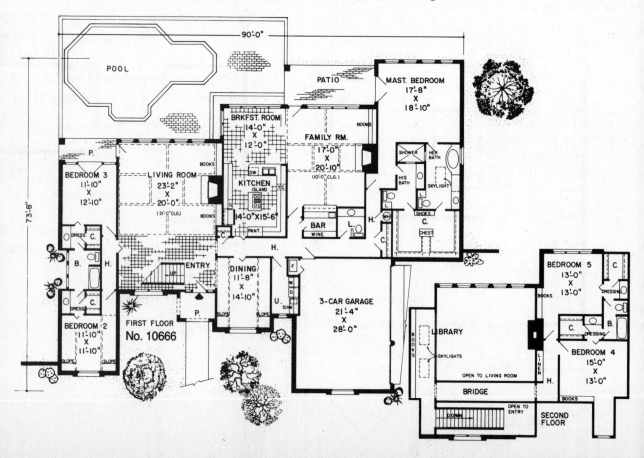

Bridge Adds Interior Drama

No. 20059

An upstairs bridge overlooks the foyer and living room in this dynamic design. Both the living and dining rooms have access to the rear deck. The kitchen has an adjoining breakfast area and a large pantry. The master bedroom has a spacious bath and walk-in closet. The other two bedrooms and bath are located on the second floor.

First floor — 1,234 sq. ft.
Second floor — 520 sq. ft.
Basement — 1,234 sq. ft.
Garage — 477 sq. ft.

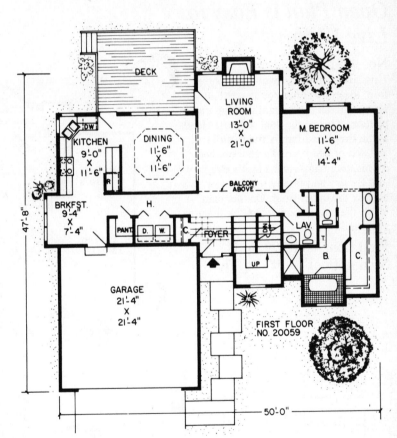

DECK

LIVING ROOM
13'-0" X 21'-0"

M. BEDROOM
11'-6" X 14'-4"

KITCHEN
9'-0" X 11'-6"

DINING
11'-6" X 11'-6"

BALCONY ABOVE

BRKFST.
9'-4" X 7'-4"

H.

PANT. D. W. C. FOYER UP LAV. B. C.

GARAGE
21'-4" X 21'-4"

47'-8"

50'-0"

FIRST FLOOR
NO. 20059

A Karl Kreeger Design

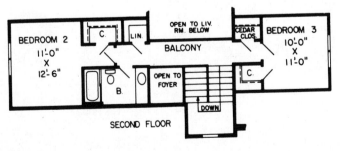

BEDROOM 2
11'-0" X 12'-6"

C. LIN

OPEN TO LIV. RM. BELOW

BALCONY

CEDAR CLOS

BEDROOM 3
10'-0" X 11'-0"

B.

OPEN TO FOYER

C.

DOWN

SECOND FLOOR

Open Plan is Easy to Live With

No. 90522

This house on three levels, all visible from the entry, provides an open atmosphere with an eye toward flowing traffic patterns. One of the dual staircases leads to the fireplaced family room, full bath, and den or bedroom. Three more bedrooms, two baths, and a bird's eye view of the entry and family room below occupy the upper floor. On the main level, the living room and nook feature bay windows.

First floor — 1,399 sq. ft.
Second floor — 787 sq. ft.

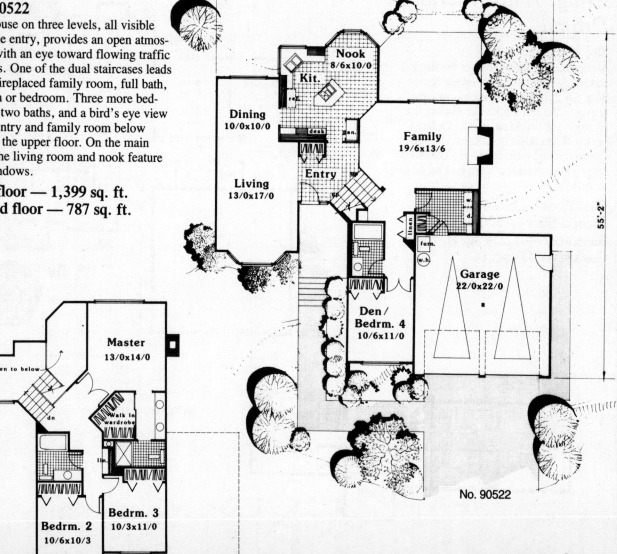

56'-0"

55'-2"

Nook
8/6x10/0

Kit.

Dining
10/0x10/0

desk

Family
19/6x13/6

Living
13/0x17/0

Entry

linen

furn.
w.h.

Den /
Bedrm. 4
10/6x11/0

Garage
22/0x22/0

No. 90522

Master
13/0x14/0

open to below

dn

Walk in
wardrobe

lin.

Bedrm. 2
10/6x10/3

Bedrm. 3
10/3x11/0

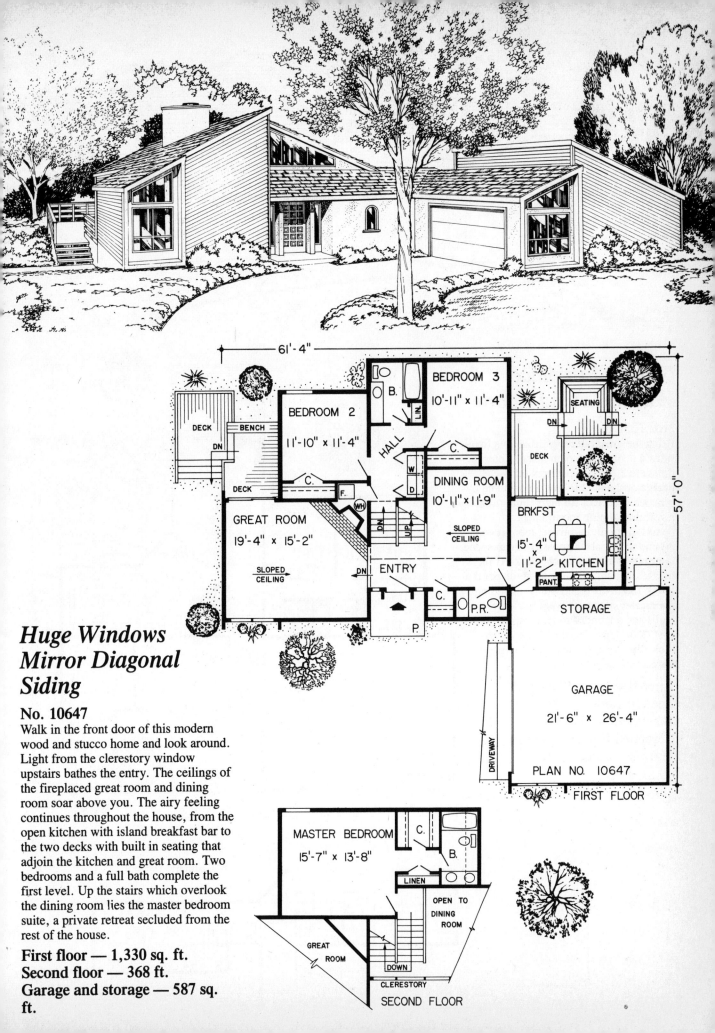

Huge Windows
Mirror Diagonal
Siding

No. 10647

Walk in the front door of this modern
wood and stucco home and look around.
Light from the clerestory window
upstairs bathes the entry. The ceilings of
the fireplaced great room and dining
room soar above you. The airy feeling
continues throughout the house, from the
open kitchen with island breakfast bar to
the two decks with built in seating that
adjoin the kitchen and great room. Two
bedrooms and a full bath complete the
first level. Up the stairs which overlook
the dining room lies the master bedroom
suite, a private retreat secluded from the
rest of the house.

First floor — 1,330 sq. ft.
Second floor — 368 ft.
Garage and storage — 587 sq.
ft.

BEDROOM 3
10'-11" x 11'-4"

SEATING

BEDROOM 2
11'-10" x 11'-4"

B.

LIN.

HALL

C.

W
D

DINING ROOM
10'-11" x 11'-9"

DECK

BENCH

DECK

DN

DN

DN

DECK

C.

F.

WH

GREAT ROOM
19'-4" x 15'-2"

SLOPED
CEILING

DN

UP

SLOPED
CEILING

BRKFST

15'-4"
x
11'-2"   KITCHEN

PANT.

STORAGE

SLOPED CEILING

DN

ENTRY

C.

P.R.

P.

DRIVEWAY

GARAGE
21'-6" x 26'-4"

PLAN NO. 10647

FIRST FLOOR

61'-4"

57'-0"

MASTER BEDROOM
15'-7" x 13'-8"

C.

B.

LINEN

OPEN TO
DINING
ROOM

GREAT
ROOM

DOWN

CLERESTORY

SECOND FLOOR

Corner Fireplace
Warms Living Room

No. 10581

Bring the great outdoors inside this luxurious 4 bedroom, 3 bath home. Enter the dramatic 2-story foyer from the 3-car garage or the double front doors. The living area is perfect for entertaining. Parlor, formal dining room, kitchen, breakfast room, and living room revolve around a central staircase. You can spend your outdoor hours on the deck off the breakfast room or screened porch off the living room. Two bedrooms, including the master suite with walk-in closet, two baths and a laundry room complete the first floor. Upstairs, the balcony overlooks the foyer and leads to two more bedrooms and a full bath.

First floor — 1,916 sq. ft.
Second floor — 740 sq. ft.
Basement — 1,916 sq. ft.
Screened Porch — 192 sq. ft.
Garage — 814 sq. ft.

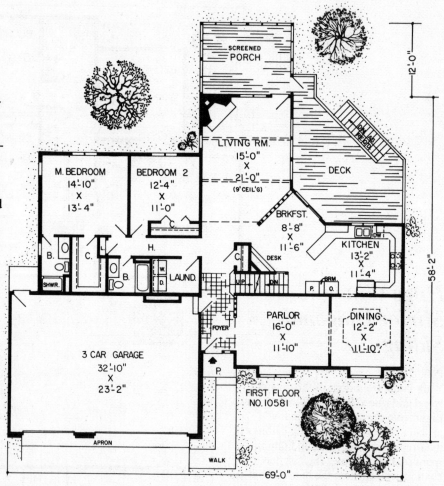

A Karl Kreeger Design

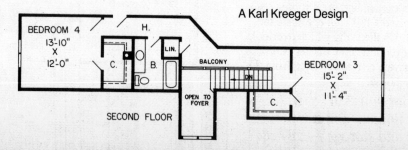

Victorian Details Enhance Facade

No. 10593

A charming porch shelters the entrance of this four bedroom home with country kitchen. In colder climates, the closed vestibule cuts heat loss. Off the central foyer, the cozy living room shares a fireplace with the family room, which contains a bar and access to the patio and screened porch for entertaining. The bay windowed breakfast room is handy for quick meals. Or, use the formal dining room with octagonal recessed ceiling. All the bedrooms, located on the second floor, have walk-in closets.

First floor — 1,450 sq. ft.
Second floor — 1,341 sq. ft.
Basement — 1,450 sq. ft.
Garage — 629 sq. ft.
Covered porch — 144 sq. ft.

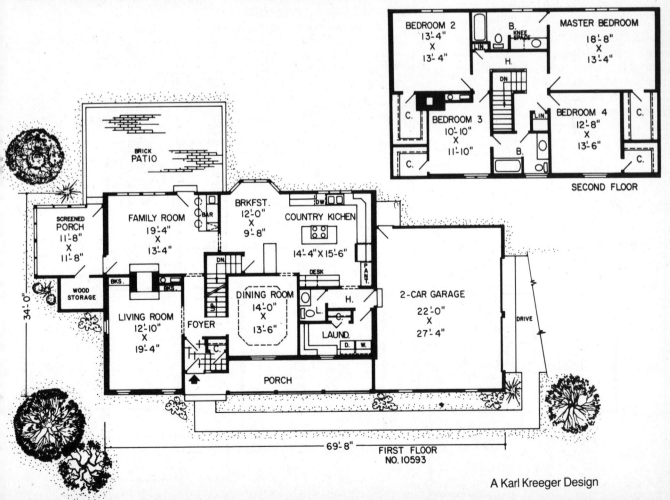

A Karl Kreeger Design

Covered Porch Offered in Farm-type Traditional

No. 20064

This pleasant traditional design has a farmhouse flavor exterior that incorporates a covered porch and features a circle wood louver on its garage, giving this design a feeling of sturdiness. Inside on the first level from the foyer and to the right is a formal dining room complete with a bay window and an elevated ceiling and a corner china cabinet. To the left of the foyer is the living room with a wood-burning fireplace. The kitchen is connected to the breakfast room and there is a room for the laundry facilities. A half bath is also featured on the first floor. The second floor has three bedrooms. The master bedroom is on the second floor and has its own private bath and walk-in closet. The other two bedrooms share a full bath. A two-car garage is also added into this design.

First floor — 892 sq. ft.
Second floor — 836 sq. ft.
Basement — 892 sq. ft.
Garage — 491 sq. ft.

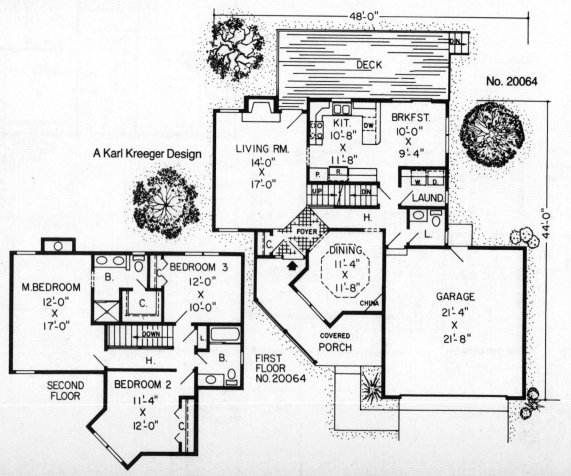

A Karl Kreeger Design

Lunch by the Pool

No. 10696

After a day of sun and swimming, you'll enjoy retreating to the master wing with skylit bath, room-sized closets, and quiet, book-lined study. But when you're in the mood to entertain, this convenient floor plan guarantees success. Greet your guests in the foyer and lead them into the formal living room or family room with adjoining bar and patio. The island kitchen, with its huge pantry and breakfast nook overlooking the pool, has plenty of room for more than one cook. A cozy library at the top of the stairs leads to three more bedrooms and two full baths.

First floor — 3,252 sq. ft.
Second floor — 873 sq. ft.
Garage — 746 sq. ft.

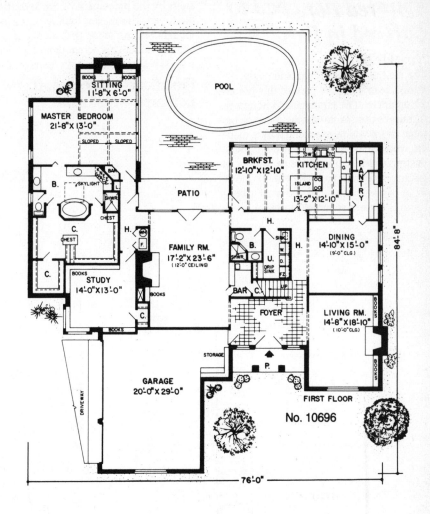

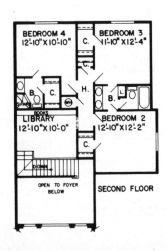

Spiral Stairs Lead to Loft

No. 90127

The central A-frame of this unusual design comprises the core of this home's living areas. The large eat-in kitchen easily serves the formal dining room or the great room which is accented by a cathedral ceiling, fireplace and sliding doors leading to the patio. Three bedrooms and a four-piece bath are gathered on one wing of the home while the master bedroom is further separated from the living areas by the placement of the laundry and the foyer. The master bath features individual dressing areas with a central bathing area. This arrangement is ideal for a working couple with teenagers.

First floor — 2,093 sq. ft.
Loft area — 326 sq. ft.

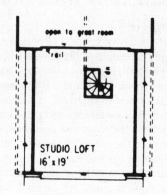

open to great room

rail

STUDIO LOFT
16' x 19'

Loft Area

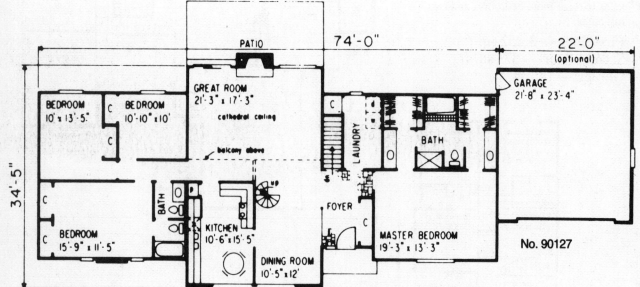

PATIO

74'-0"

22'-0"
(optional)

GREAT ROOM
21'-3" x 17'-3"
cathedral ceiling

GARAGE
21'-8" x 23'-4"

BEDROOM
10' x 13'-5"

BEDROOM
10'-10" x 10'

C

balcony above

LAUNDRY

BATH

34'-5"

BATH

BEDROOM
15'-9" x 11'-5"

KITCHEN
10'-6" x 15'-5"

FOYER

MASTER BEDROOM
19'-3" x 13'-3"

No. 90127

DINING ROOM
10'-5" x 12'

FIRST FLOOR WITH BASEMENT

Den, Third Bedroom Possibilities

No. 19766

Equipped with closets and access to a half-bath, the sizable study on the first floor of this shake shingle traditional is equally adapted to use as a den or third bedroom. The 27 foot living-dining room shows an abundance of space and small paned windows as well as a wood-burning fireplace. For step saving efficiency the kitchen complex includes a breakfast room, laundry and pantry.

First floor — 1,071 sq. ft.
Second floor — 572 sq. ft.
Basement — 966 sq. ft.
Garage — 575 sq. ft.

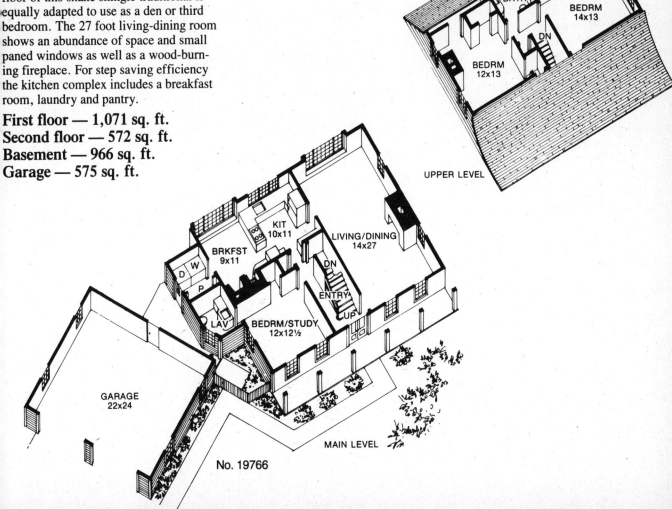

Sunny and Warm

No. 91029

Here's a home unlike any you've ever seen. The multi-level plan unfolds as you walk through the foyer. You'll find a handy den on this floor. Four steps up, active areas revolve around a hexagonal hallway, giving every room a distinctive shape. Mealtimes are a breeze with the pass-through between the island kitchen and dining room. Fireplaces keep formal and family living areas toasty even on the coldest days. And, when the weather's nice, the rear deck is a great place to relax. The other staircase off the foyer winds its way up to four spacious bedrooms. Look at the raised spa and double vanities in the master suite. A home this special is hard to resist.

First floor — 1,638 sq. ft.
Second floor — 1,210 sq. ft.

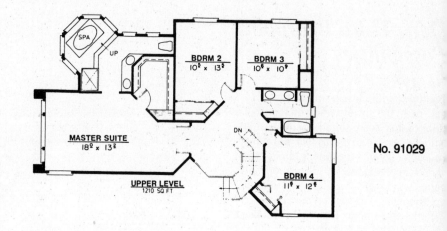

No. 91029

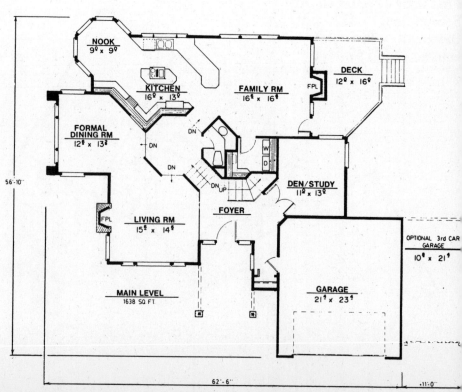

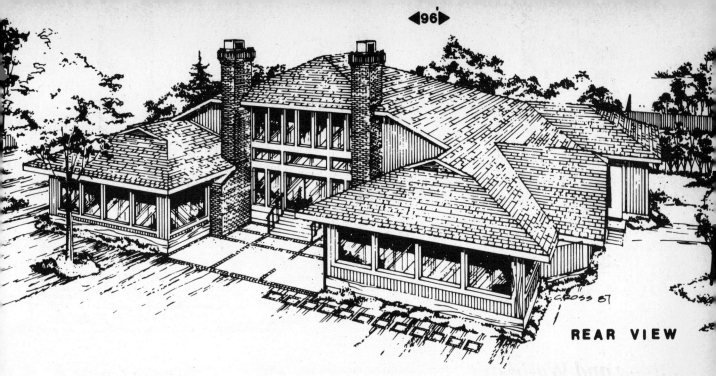

◄96'►

REAR VIEW

Two Lofts Provide Private Perches

No. 91302

Here's an outstanding, energy-saving home with loads of contemporary appeal. The airlock vestibule leads to a soaring, two story entry, brilliantly iluminated by a window wall at the rear of the house. The fireplaced living and family rooms share the same sunwashed atmosphere. Notice the location of the elegant, elevated dining room, just across the hall from the cheerful kitchen with convenient island eating bar. Climb the stairs off the entry, put your feet up, and survey active areas and the back yard from your lofty vantage point. The master suite, down a hallway off the entry, features a luxurious bath with sauna. Walk past the handy utility room to reach the other bedrooms.

Main level — 4,096 sq. ft.
Loft — 360 sq. ft.

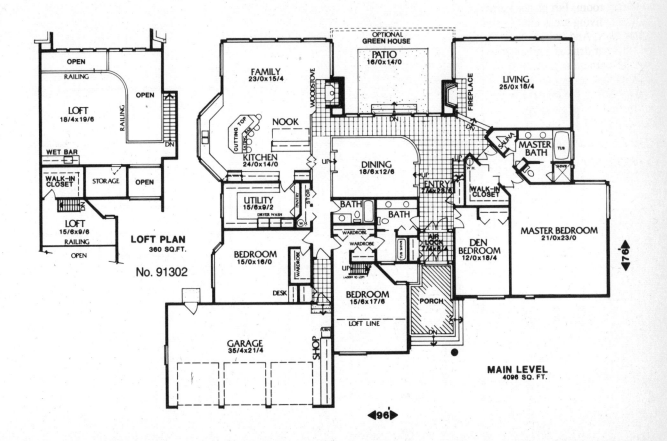

LOFT PLAN
360 SQ. FT.

No. 91302

MAIN LEVEL
4096 SQ. FT.

◄96'►

Compact, but Elegant

No. 20077

You'll never get bored with the rooms in this charming, three-bedroom Victorian. The angular plan gives every room an interesting shape. From the wrap-around veranda, the entry foyer leads through the living room and parlor, breaking them up without confining them, and giving each room an airy atmosphere. In the dining room, with its hexagonal recessed ceiling, you can enjoy your after-dinner coffee and watch the kids playing on the deck. Or eat in the sunny breakfast room off the island kitchen, where every wall has a window, and every window has a different view. You'll love the master suite's bump-out windows, walk-in closets, and double sinks.

First floor — 1,393 sq. ft.
Second floor — 1,096 sq. ft.
Basement — 1,393 sq. ft.
Garage — 491 sq. ft.

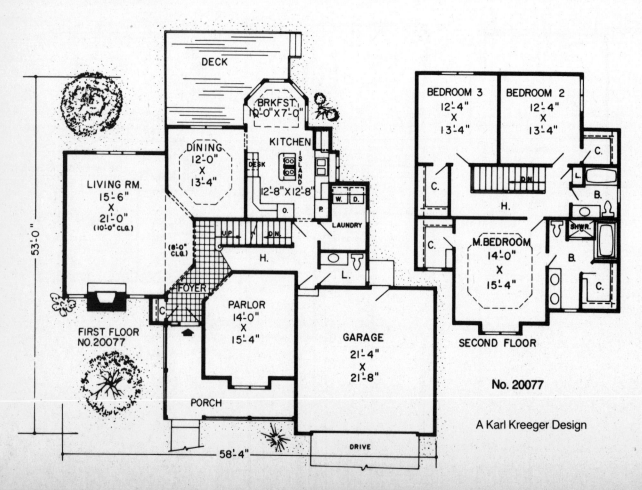

A Karl Kreeger Design

Built-In Planter Surrounds Split Level

No. 90916

Here's a house on three levels that's brimming with features. The master suite boasts a walk-through dressing area and a 3/4 bath. The family bath is huge, and contains a practical double-basin vanity for hectic mornings. Looking from the breakfast area through a railing into the sunken family room, the visual effect is spectacular. And, the convenient, central kitchen location makes food service to all the living areas a breeze.

Main floor — 1,350 sq. ft.
Second floor — 648 sq. ft.
Unfinished basement —
704 sq. ft.
Garage — 418 sq. ft.
Width — 48 ft.
Depth — 52 ft.

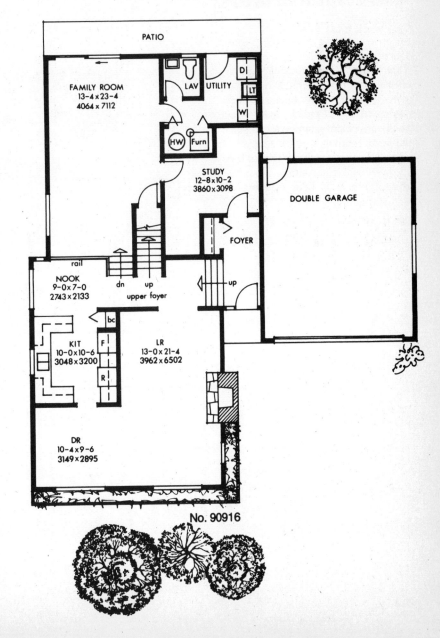

No. 90916

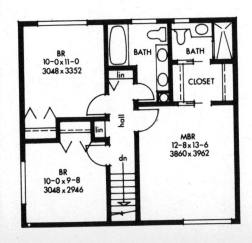

Master Suite Features Cozy Hearth

No. 10635

Columns adorn the classic entry of this traditional colonial dwelling. A hallway, flanked by the living room and beamed family room with fireplace, leads directly into the convenient island kitchen. Eat in the formal dining room or sunny dinette. Sliding glass doors lead to the patio for outside entertaining. Four bedrooms and two baths lie at the top of the central staircase.

First floor — 1,280 sq. ft.
Second floor — 1,224 sq. ft.
Basement — 1,283 sq. ft.
Garage — 576 sq. ft.

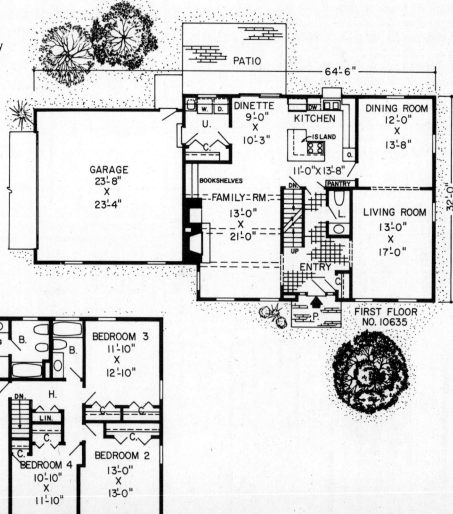

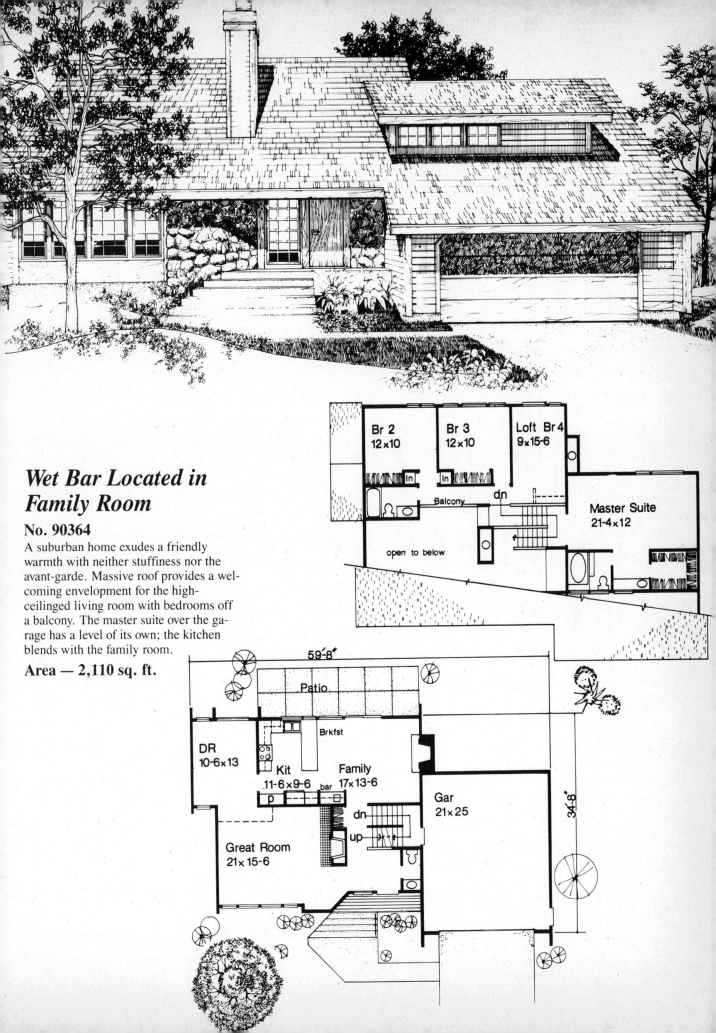

Wet Bar Located in Family Room

No. 90364

A suburban home exudes a friendly warmth with neither stuffiness nor the avant-garde. Massive roof provides a welcoming envelopment for the high-ceilinged living room with bedrooms off a balcony. The master suite over the garage has a level of its own; the kitchen blends with the family room.

Area — 2,110 sq. ft.

Br 2
12×10

Br 3
12×10

Loft Br 4
9×15-6

in

in

Balcony

dn

Master Suite
21-4×12

open to below

59'-8"

Patio

Brkfst

DR
10-6×13

Kit
11-6×9-6

Family
17×13-6

bar

Gar
21×25

34'-8"

p

dn

Great Room
21×15-6

up

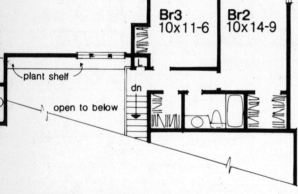

Br3
10x11-6

Br2
10x14-9

Upper Floor

plant shelf

open to below

dn

Four Bedroom 1 1/2 Story Design

No. 90358

Many of todays single family markets are looking for a flexible plan that grows and adapts to their families changing needs. This is such a house with its master bedroom and den/4th bedroom down, double bedrooms up, stacked baths and well working open and flowing living areas. The exterior impact is of hi-style, hi-value; the interior impact is highlighted by the vaulted living room and thru views to the rear deck and yard. This house belongs in a neighborhood where the custom exterior look will make for a surprising space/value combination to the move up young family market.

Main floor — 1,062 sq. ft.
Upper floor — 469 sq. ft.

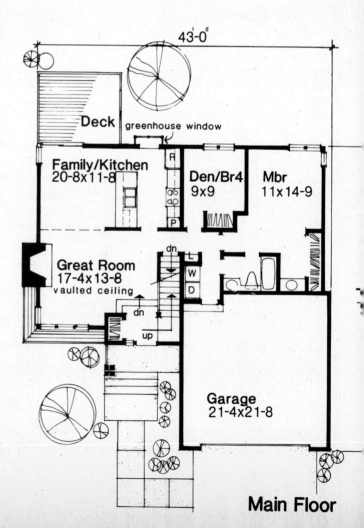

43-0"

Deck   greenhouse window

Family/Kitchen
20-8x11-8

Den/Br4
9x9

Mbr
11x14-9

Great Room
17-4x13-8
vaulted ceiling

dn

dn

up

W
D

Garage
21-4x21-8

Main Floor

Two Bedrooms Tucked Upstairs

No. 91235

Here's a marvelous approach to family living. This four-bedroom stucco beauty is zoned according to use into family, formal, and quiet areas. And, each zone is easily accessed from the central foyer. Walk left to the family wing, with its beamed family room, kitchen, laundry, and breakfast bay. Straight ahead, formal areas feature French doors that open to the terrace. You'll appreciate the cozy convenience built-in bookcases, a fireplace, and a wetbar give the living room. The first-floor bedroom wing includes a luxurious master suite. French doors flanking the fireplace open to the terrace; two walk-in closets create a hallway that leads into a greenhouse bath with shower, bath, and twin vanities.

First floor — 2,907 sq. ft.
Second floor — 735 sq. ft.
Unfinished basement — 1,034 sq. ft.
Garage — 491 sq. ft.

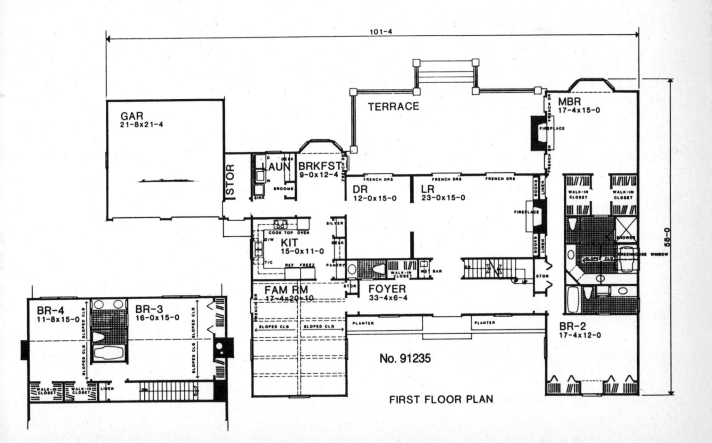

No. 91235

FIRST FLOOR PLAN

Octagon Sitting Room

No. 10418

Imagine relaxing in your sitting room in front of a hearty fire after a leisure shower or bath, then snuggling into bed for a long night's rest, all without ever leaving your master bedroom suite and its comforts. Lines from the sitting room's octagon shape position the fireplace at an angle and carry over into the bath and hallway to add angled diversity to these areas. Windows here, as well as in the living center and dining room, are a full 8 feet. Raised hearth fireplace, exposed beams, built-in bookshelves, and patio access are features of the 18 x 23 living center, open opposite the fireplace to the entry way. Ceilings of the entry rise two stories and watch over a short bridgeway linking stairs to the second level rooms.

First floor — 2,600 sq. ft.
Second floor — 854 sq. ft.
Garage — 638 sq. ft.
Patio & Porch — 354 sq. ft.

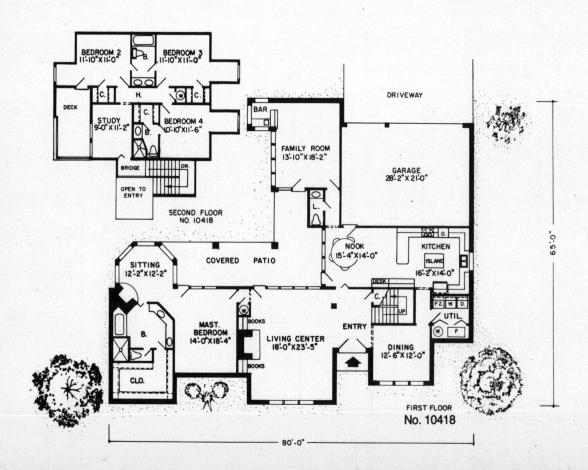

Family Kitchen Highlight

No. 90319

Bring the family together in this large family kitchen. The food preparation area is designed for maximum counter and cabinet space. There's even a coat closet next to the garage entrance and a built-in pantry. The bump out window is an ideal location for the dining table, and the laundry is hidden in a closet. In addition to a living room with window-flanked fireplace, the first floor also includes the large master bedroom suite. The two story entry unifies this design by incorporating two skylights. A third skylight enhances one of the second floor bedrooms.

Main level — 876 sq. ft.
Upper level — 504 sq. ft.
Basement — 859 sq. ft.
Garage — 436 sq. ft.

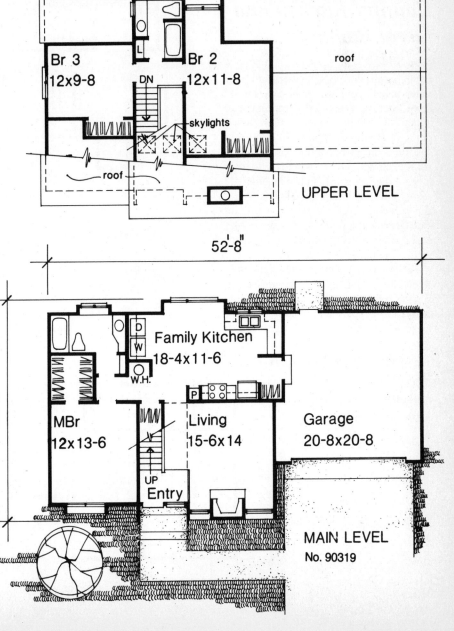

UPPER LEVEL

Br 3
12x9-8

Br 2
12x11-8

roof

DN

skylights

roof

52'-8"

29'-8"

Family Kitchen
18-4x11-6

MBr
12x13-6

Living
15-6x14

Garage
20-8x20-8

W.H.

P

UP

Entry

MAIN LEVEL

No. 90319

Country Kitchen and Great Room

No. 90419

Front porch, dormers, shutters and multi-paned windows on the exterior of this Cape Cod design are complimented by an informal interior. The main floor is divided into three sections. In the first section is an eat-in country kitchen with island counter and bay window and a large utility room which can be entered from either the kitchen or garage. The second section is the great room with inside fireplace, an informal dining nook and double doors opening onto the rear deck. The master suite features a walk-in closet and compartmentalized bath with linen closet. The upper floor consists of a second full bath and two bedrooms with ample closet space and window seats. A large storage area is provided over the garage.

First floor — 1,318 sq. ft.
Second floor — 718 sq. ft.
Basement — 1,221 sq. ft.
Garage — 436 sq. ft.

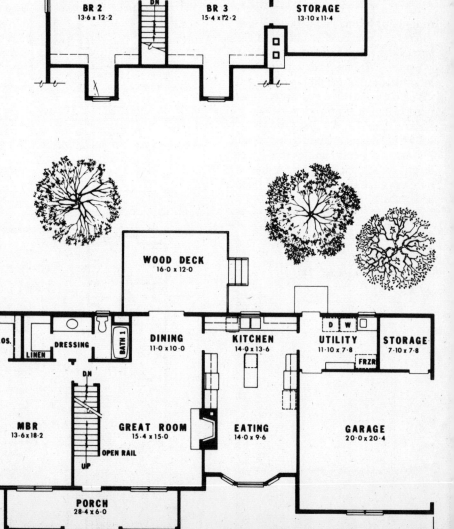

Cathedral Ceiling With Studio

No. 90420

This rustic/contemporary modified A-Frame design combines a high cathedral ceiling over a sunken living room with a large studio over the two rear bedrooms. The isolated master suite features a walk-in closet and compartmentalized bath with double vanity and linen closet. The two rear bedrooms include ample closet space and share a unique bath-and-a-half arrangement. On one side of the U-shaped kitchen and breakfast nook is the formal dining room which is separated from the entry by a planter. On the other side is a utility room which can be entered from either the kitchen or garage. The exterior features a massive stone fireplace, large glass areas and a combination of vertical wood siding and stone.

First floor — 1,860 sq. ft.
Second floor — 343 sq. ft.

STUDIO
13'-0×20'-0

BALCONY

DOWN

OPEN RAIL

LIVING AREA BELOW

BEDROOM
12-0×12-0

BEDROOM
12-0×12-0

DINING
11-0×12-6

KITCHEN
11-0×14-0

GARAGE
20-0×20-6

BATH

CLOSET

CLOSET

BATH

BEDROOM
14-0×20-6

LINEN

CLOS

DOWN

UP

PLANTER

45'-8"

CLOSET

OPEN RAIL

OPEN RAIL

ENTRY

CLOS

BREAKFAST
11-0×10-0

UTILITY
10-0×6-0

STORAGE
10-0×6-0

SUNKEN LIVING AREA
24-6×18-0

Kitchen Is Gourmet's Heaven

No. 10417

Inside and out, this design speaks of space and luxury. Outside, cedar shake roofing contrasts nicely with brick veneer to compliment arched and leaded windows and false dormers. Double entry doors usher you into a two-story entrance with staircase curving gently to second level rooms. Ten-foot ceilings throughout the lower level and nine-foot ceilings upstairs add to the spaciousness already created by large rooms. And, look at these kitchen features — 60 sq. ft. of counter space, a 5 x 6 step-saving island cooking range, a desk area, a windowed eating nook, and nearby patio access.

First floor — 3,307 sq. ft.
Second floor — 837 sq. ft.
Garage — 646 sq. ft.
Porch and Patios — 382 sq. ft.

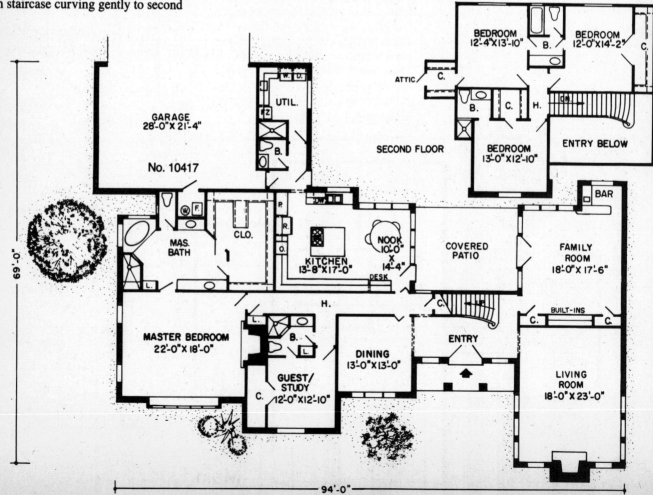

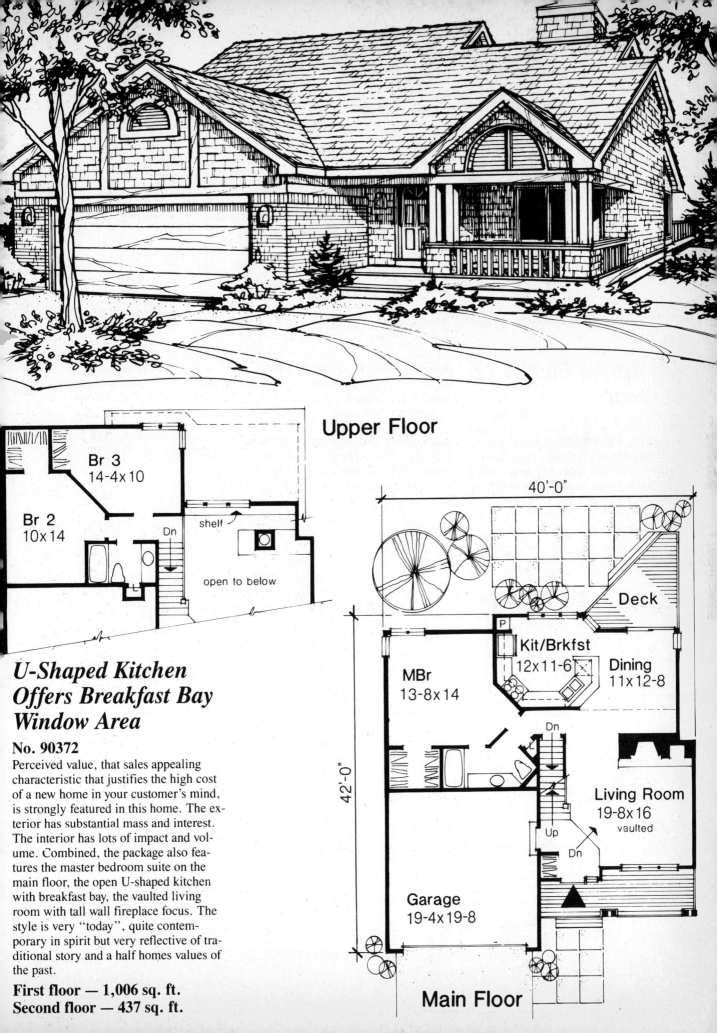

Upper Floor

Br 3
14-4 x 10

Br 2
10 x 14

shelf

Dn

open to below

U-Shaped Kitchen Offers Breakfast Bay Window Area

No. 90372

Perceived value, that sales appealing characteristic that justifies the high cost of a new home in your customer's mind, is strongly featured in this home. The exterior has substantial mass and interest. The interior has lots of impact and volume. Combined, the package also features the master bedroom suite on the main floor, the open U-shaped kitchen with breakfast bay, the vaulted living room with tall wall fireplace focus. The style is very "today", quite contemporary in spirit but very reflective of traditional story and a half homes values of the past.

First floor — 1,006 sq. ft.
Second floor — 437 sq. ft.

40'-0"

Deck

P

Kit/Brkfst
12 x 11-6

Dining
11 x 12-8

MBr
13-8 x 14

Dn

42'-0"

Living Room
19-8 x 16
vaulted

Up

Dn

Garage
19-4 x 19-8

Main Floor

Perfect for Parties

No. 10663

Does your family enjoy entertaining? Here's your home! This handsome, rambling beauty can handle a crowd of any size. Greet your guests in a beautiful foyer that opens to the cozy, bayed living room and elegant dining room with floor-to-ceiling windows. Show them the impressive two-story gallery and book-lined study, flooded with sunlight from atrium doors and clerestory windows. Or, gather around the fire in the vaulted family room. The bar connects to the efficient kitchen, just steps away from both nook and formal dining room. And, when the guests go home, you'll appreci-ate your luxurious first-floor master suite and the cozy upstairs bedroom suites with adjoining sitting room.

First floor — 2,446 sq. ft.
Second floor — 844 sq. ft.
Garage — 660 sq. ft.

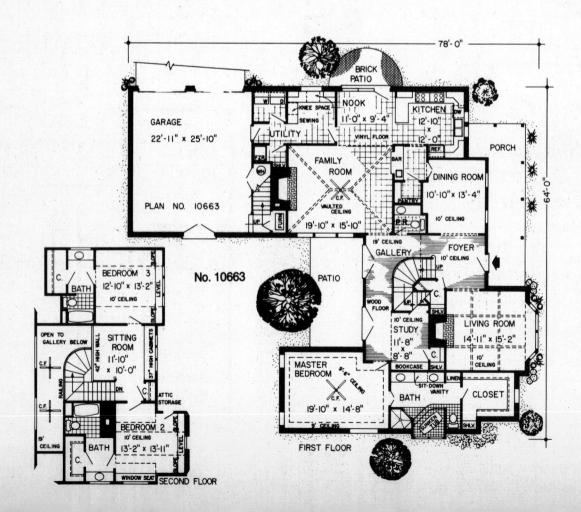

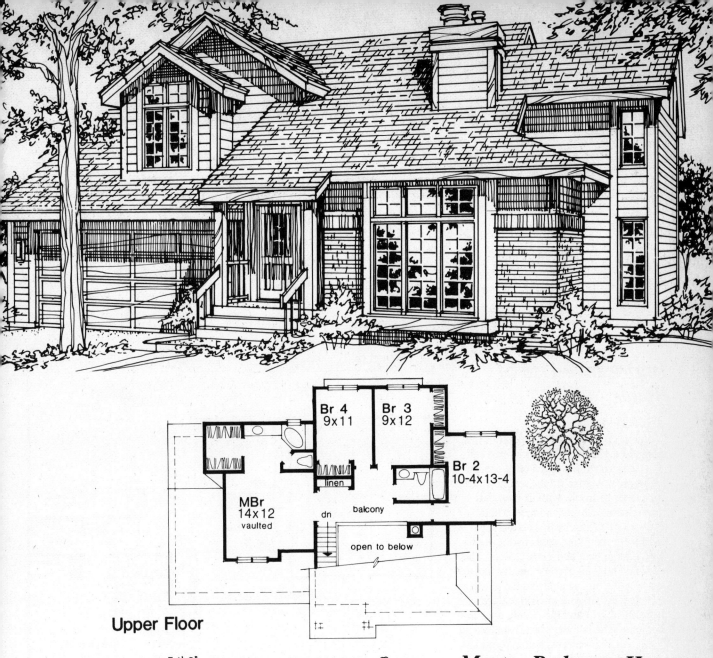

Upper Floor

Br 4
9x11

Br 3
9x12

Br 2
10-4x13-4

linen

MBr
14x12
vaulted

dn   balcony

open to below

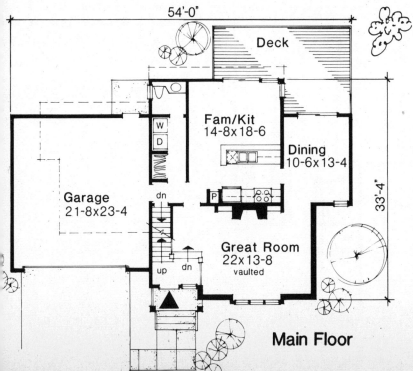

54'-0"

Deck

Fam/Kit
14-8x18-6

Dining
10-6x13-4

W
D

Garage
21-8x23-4

dn

33'-4"

up   dn

Great Room
22x13-8
vaulted

P

Main Floor

Master Bedroom Has a Vaulted Ceiling

No. 90371

Young families and the move up market are looking for lots of liveable space in a good looking package that combines a look of substance with sophistication. This kind of house has that design character with an exterior that uses masonry and rough siding under a sweeping roof line, an interior that lets space flow and accepts high impact views. The entry and great room vault up to the hall balcony above, the country kitchen is great for family doings, the master bedroom suite emphasizes good walk in closet space and a luxurious bathroom. And note how well the house hugs the ground line for a two story home, a look that makes the house one of the 80's generation.

First floor — 952 sq. ft.
Second floor — 915 sq. ft.

Impressive Use of Space

No. 90131

The great room is the focal point of this uniquely organized plan; its sloped ceiling rises two stories to the cozy second floor balcony. Also on the second floor is the master bedroom with its own balcony, double closets and roomy bath. The two first floor bedrooms are separated from the living areas by the stairway, a large bath and extra closets. The L-shaped kitchen is conveniently located between the dining area and the garage entrance. Additional kitchen features are the built-in grill and the sliding door to the patio. The laundry room is placed so that it can also serve as a mud room just inside the garage door.

First floor — 1,320 sq. ft.
Second floor — 444 sq. ft.

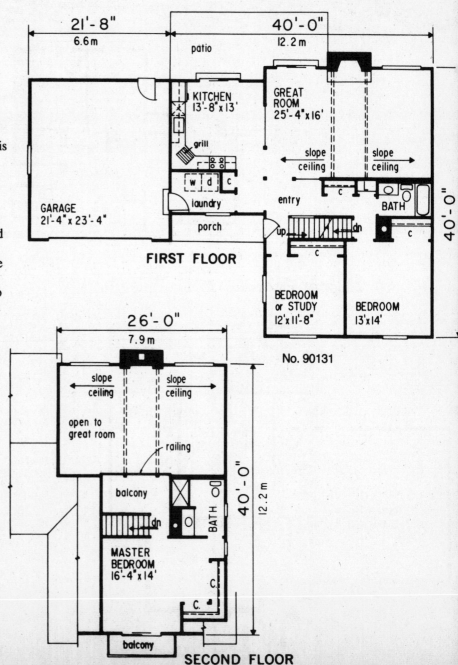

Cozy Two-Story Contemporary

No. 10475

This is a house for today that will fit into any neighborhood. Its clean lines and simple design make it a delight to the eye. Practicality and thoughtful planning make living in this house naturally comfortable. Room placement deals realistically with family needs. The family room and living room are separate to keep activities in one room from overlapping into the other. On the sleeping level, none of the bedrooms shares a common wall, so quiet and individual interests are enhanced. The kitchen opens into the family room. Sliding doors in the dining and family rooms lead to a possible patio or deck. A powder room finishes off the main level.

Main level — 894 sq. ft.
Upper level — 820 sq. ft.
Basement — 894 sq. ft.
Garage — 476 sq. ft.

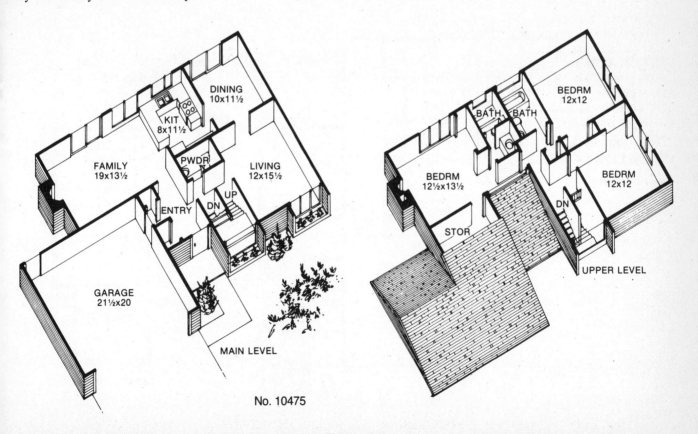

No. 10475

Porch Recalls a Romantic Era

No. 20098

Arched windows and a two-story bay lend an air of elegance to this exceptional four-bedroom beauty. Interior spaces are characterized by distinctive ceiling treatments, sloping ceilings pierced by skylights, and efficient room placements.

Notice how easily the kitchen serves the hexagonal breakfast room, the formal dining room, and the adjoining deck. Even the fireplaced living room is only steps away. And, when the alarm rings early in the morning, you'll be grateful for the master suite's proximity to the coffee pot. The staircase off the foyer leads to three more bedrooms and a full, skylit bath with double vanities. Be sure to notice the wonderful angles and generous closet space in each room.

First floor — 1,843 sq. ft.
Second floor — 1039 sq. ft.
Basement — 1,843 sq. ft.
Garage — 484 sq. ft.

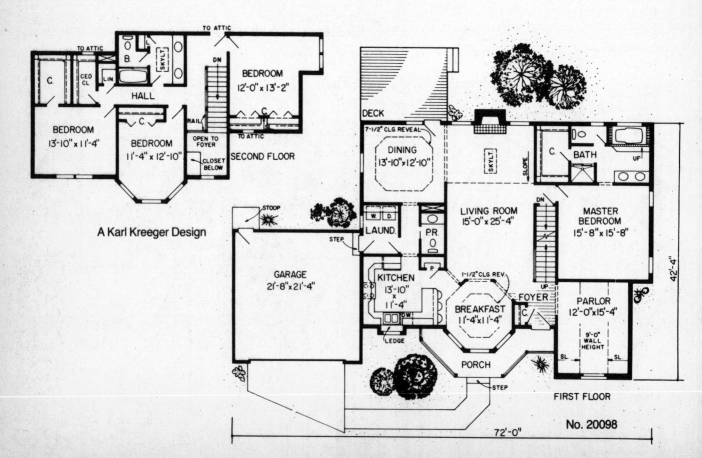

A Karl Kreeger Design

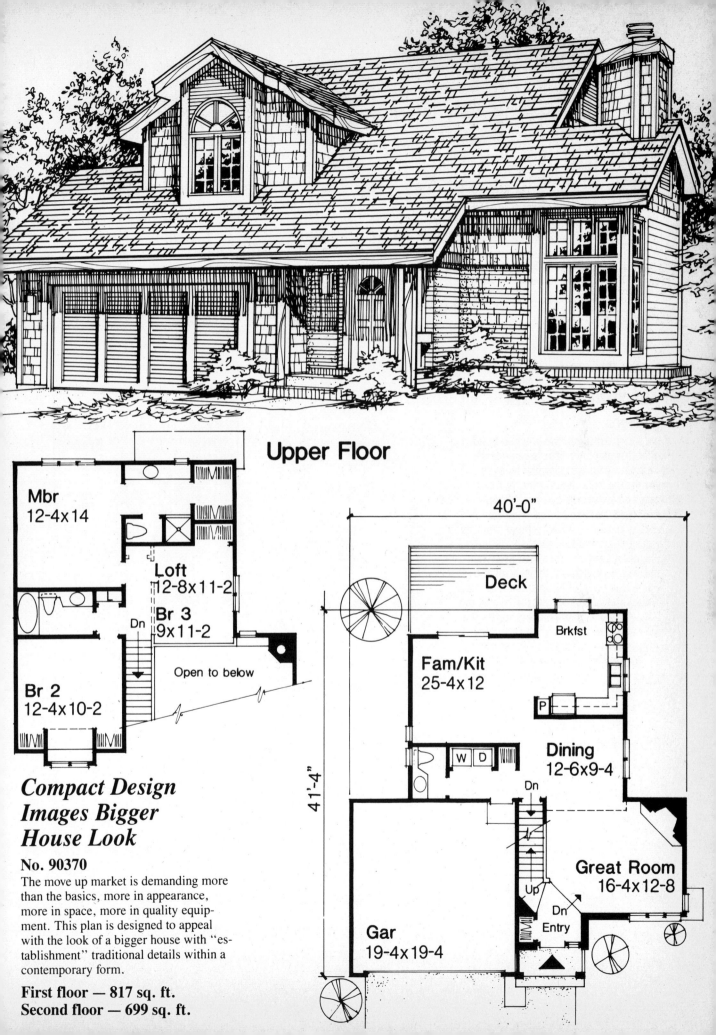

Upper Floor

Mbr
12-4x14

Loft
12-8x11-2

Br 3
9x11-2

Dn

Open to below

Br 2
12-4x10-2

40'-0"

Deck

Brkfst

Fam/Kit
25-4x12

P

W D

Dining
12-6x9-4

Dn

41'-4"

Up

Dn

Entry

Gar
19-4x19-4

Great Room
16-4x12-8

Compact Design Images Bigger House Look

No. 90370

The move up market is demanding more than the basics, more in appearance, more in space, more in quality equipment. This plan is designed to appeal with the look of a bigger house with "establishment" traditional details within a contemporary form.

First floor — 817 sq. ft.
Second floor — 699 sq. ft.

Friendly Porch Welcomes Guests

No. 91206

Here's a charming home you can build now and finish later. The area over the garage houses great potential as a play room for the kids. And, with four bedrooms and two baths upstairs, there's plenty of room for your growing family. The master suite features a huge, walk-in closet, a cozy window seat, and double sinks and a garden tub as well as a walk-in shower. Downstairs, the central entry opens to the formal living room and leads to a sunken family room at the rear of the house. A bank of french doors unites the family and dining rooms with the back yard. Steps away from the dining room, the country kitchen features a cooktop island, a convenient breakfast bay, and a large pantry.

First floor — 1,346 sq. ft.
Second floor — 1,230 sq. ft.
Garage and storage — 788 sq. ft.

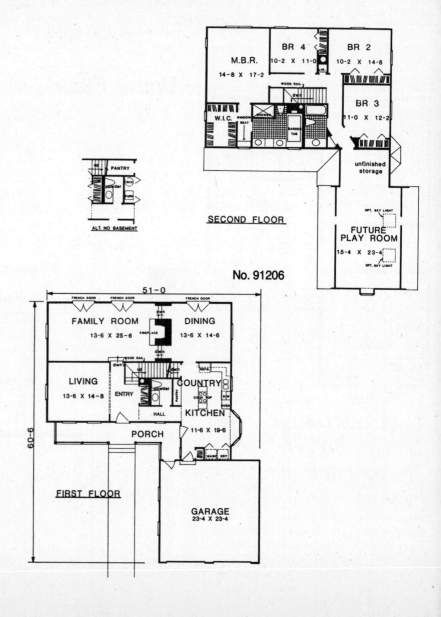

Built-In Entertainment Center for Family Fun

No. 90615

Up-to-date features bring this center hall colonial into the 20th century. The focus of the Early American living room is a heat-circulating fireplace, framed by decorative pilasters that support dropped beams. Both dining areas open to the rear terrace through sliding glass doors. And, the convenient mud room provides access to the two car garage. Four bedrooms and two baths, including the spacious master suite, occupy the second floor.

Total living area — 1,973 sq. ft.
Garage — 441 sq. ft.
(optional slab construction available)

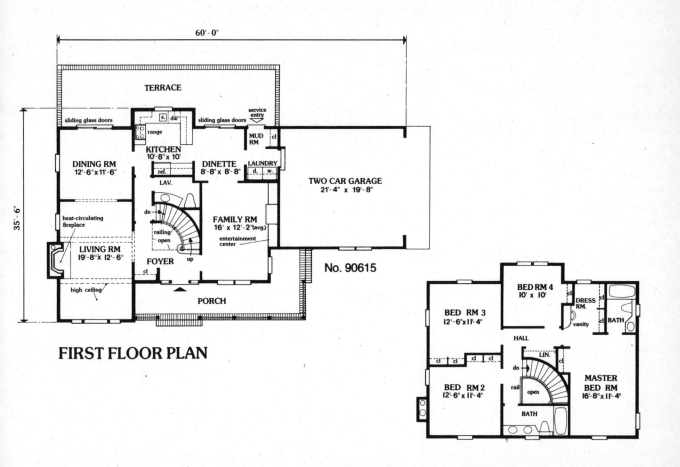

FIRST FLOOR PLAN

SECOND FLOOR PLAN

Contemporary Tudor Castle

No. 10620

Touches of old England abound in this elegant 4 bedroom, 3 1/2 bath home. Find wonderful angles, a large fireplace and rough hewn beams in the two story great room. Octagonal recessed ceilings in the master bedroom and formal dining room, and a library with built-in bookcase are traditional features borrowed from long ago. But, the luxury of a sunken skylit tub in the master suite and soaring views of the great room and foyer from the balcony are strictly contemporary. The kitchen features a convenient island design and a walk-in pantry for extra storage, with easy access to the laundry room and garage.

First floor — 2,268 sq. ft.
Second floor — 994 sq. ft.
Basement — 2,268 sq. ft.
Garage — 603 sq. ft.

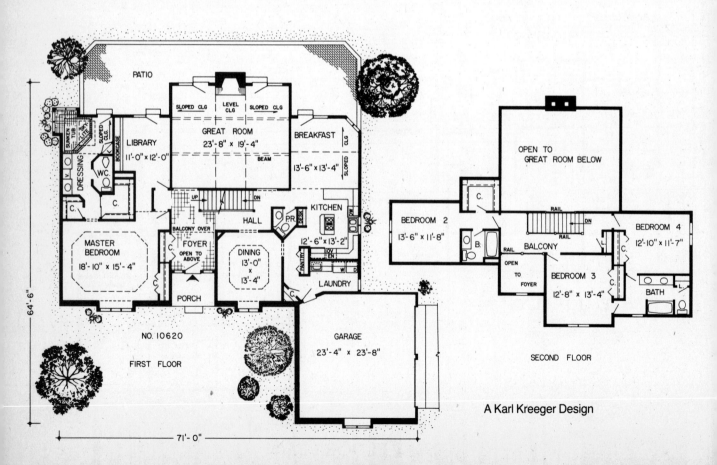

A Karl Kreeger Design

Two-Sink Baths Ease Morning Rush

No. 90622

Save energy and construction costs by building this friendly farmhouse colonial. The inviting covered porch opens to a center hall, enhanced by the stairway leading to the four-bedroom second floor. Flanked by formal living and dining rooms, the foyer leads right into the open, beamed family room, island kitchen and bay window dinette. The rear porch adjoins both family and living rooms.

First floor — 983 sq. ft.
Second floor — 1,013 sq. ft.
Mud Room — 99 sq. ft.
Garage — 481 sq. ft.
(available with or without basement)

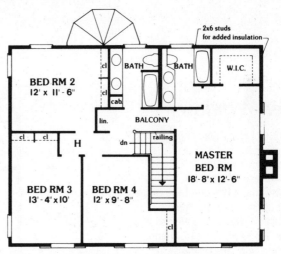

SECOND FLOOR PLAN

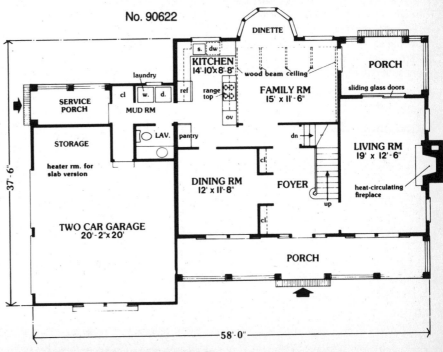

FIRST FLOOR PLAN

Dormer Windows Accent Bedroom Zone

No. 5035

Dormer windows, shutters and faithfully detailed traditional entry combine to create a unique appeal in this Cape Cod offering. Perhaps the easiest way to zone sleeping areas is to place bedrooms on a another floor, and, in this case, the result is a substantial master bedroom and two smaller bedrooms, all provided with adequate closet space. Below, the living room reaches a full 22 feet to allow plenty of room for entertaining and borders a handy half bath. Swinging doors separate kitchen and dining room.

First floor — 726 sq.ft.
Second floor — 622 sq.ft.
Basement — 726 sq.ft.

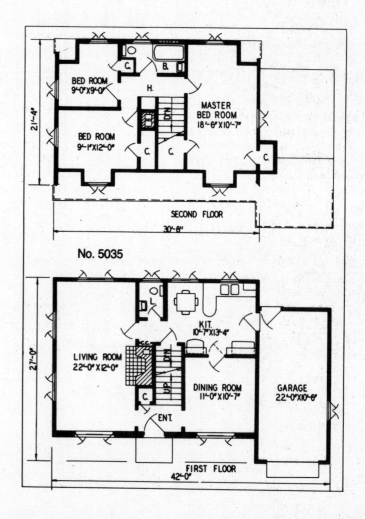

BED ROOM
9'-0"X9'-0"

BED ROOM
9'-1"X12'-0"

H.

B.

MASTER BED ROOM
18'-6"X10'-7"

SECOND FLOOR

30'-6"

21'-4"

No. 5035

LIVING ROOM
22'-0" X 12'-0"

KIT.
10'-7"X13'-4"

DINING ROOM
11'-0"X10'-7"

GARAGE
22'-0"X10'-6"

ENT.

FIRST FLOOR

42'-0"

27'-0"

A Home for All Seasons

No. 90629

The natural cedar and stone exterior of this contemporary gem is virtually maintenance free, and its dramatic lines echo the excitement inside. There are so many luxurious touches in this plan: the two-story living room overlooked by an upper-level balcony; a massive stone wall that pierces the roof and holds two fireplaces; both a kitchen oven and an outdoor barbecue. Plus, outdoor dining is a pleasure with the barbecue so handy to the kitchen. All the rooms boast outdoor decks, and each bedroom has its own. The front entrance, garage, a dressing room with bath, and laundry room occupy the lower level.

Main level — 1,001 sq. ft.
Upper level — 712 sq. ft.
Lower level — 463 sq. ft.

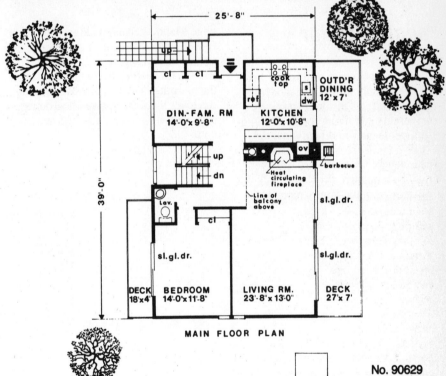

MAIN FLOOR PLAN

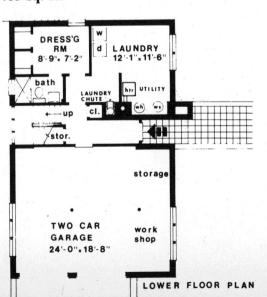

LOWER FLOOR PLAN

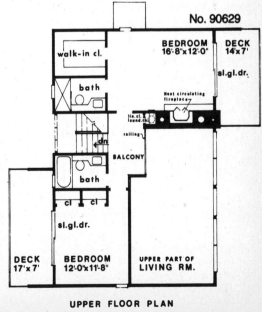

No. 90629

UPPER FLOOR PLAN

Updated Tudor

No. 20076

The traditional exterior of this four-bed-room classic only hints at the modern drama that unfolds inside. Flanked by formal dining and living rooms, the two-story foyer leads you directly into the expansive family room. There, the glass-walled view of the back yard is broken up only by a massive fireplace. Walk out to the deck from the family room or the huge island kitchen/breakfast room. The first-floor master suite is a convenience you're sure to appreciate. You won't have to travel very far to make coffee in the morning. The balcony overlooking the foyer links the upstairs bedrooms, each with a walk-in closet and nearby bath.

First floor — 2,030 sq. ft.
Second floor — 1,033 sq. ft.
Basement — 2,030 sq. ft.
Garage — 576 sq. ft.

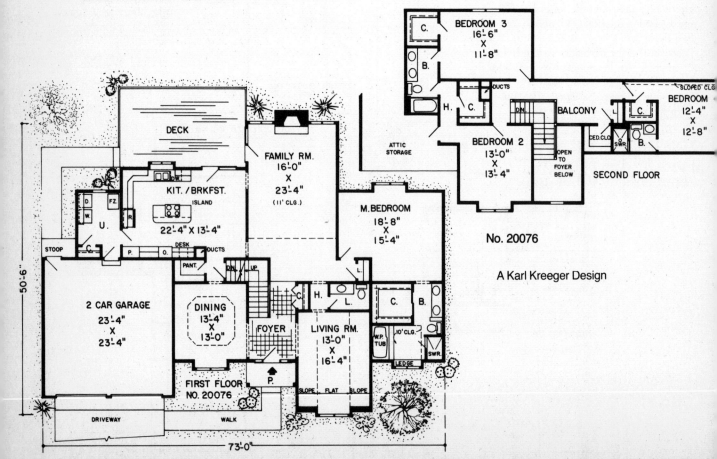

No. 20076

A Karl Kreeger Design

Bays Add Beauty and Living Space

No. 90607

The welcoming warmth that most Traditional houses seem to exude is especially evident in this center hall, four-bedroom residence. Just off the two-story foyer, the formal living room features a heat-circulating fireplace. Ionic columns and a semi-circular window wall give the dining room a classic grace. The U-shaped kitchen opens to the fireplaced family room. Off the foyer, there are two bedrooms and two baths. Two bedrooms upstairs share a bath.

First floor — 1,515 sq. ft.
Second floor — 530 sq. ft.

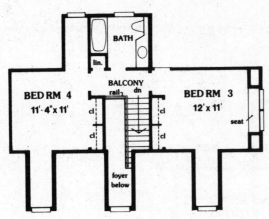

BATH
lin.

BED RM 4
11'-4" x 11'

BALCONY
rail
dn

BED RM 3
12' x 11'

cl

cl

cl

cl

seat

foyer
below

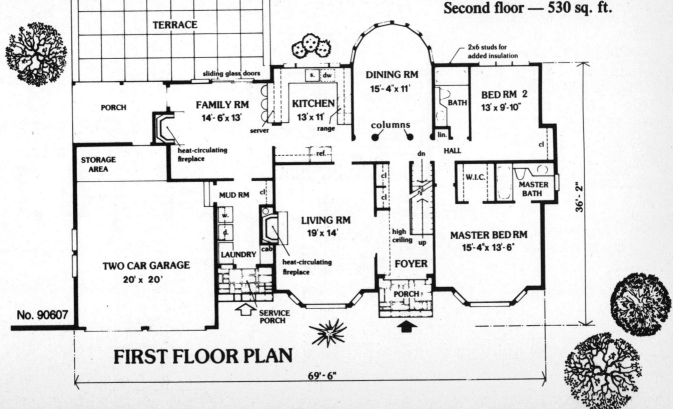

TERRACE

sliding glass doors

2x6 studs for
added insulation

DINING RM
15'-4" x 11'

BED RM 2
13' x 9'-10"

PORCH

FAMILY RM
14'-6" x 13'

KITCHEN
13' x 11'

s.   dw

range

BATH

server

columns

lin.

heat-circulating
fireplace

ref.

HALL

cl

STORAGE
AREA

MUD RM

cl

dn

W.I.C.

MASTER
BATH

w.

d.

cl

LIVING RM
19' x 14'

high
ceiling   up

MASTER BED RM
15'-4" x 13'-6"

TWO CAR GARAGE
20' x 20'

LAUNDRY

cab

heat-circulating
fireplace

FOYER

No. 90607

SERVICE
PORCH

PORCH

36'- 2"

FIRST FLOOR PLAN

69'- 6"

Dining Room Sunken One Step

No. 10420

All the stateliness and grandeur of a mansion are found in the more modest and affordable square footage of this plan. The homemaker will find the placement of the dining room, utility room, kitchen and nook in close proximity to one another, a real plus. Each of these rooms has a point of interest of its own; the dining room is sunken one step; natural light from two 3 x 3 corner windows creates a cheery work atmosphere in the utility room; counter and work space almost surround the kitchen and create a room divider between kitchen and hutched nook.

First floor — 1,727 sq. ft.
Second floor — 851 sq. ft.
Garage — 520 sq. ft.
Patio — 291 sq. ft.

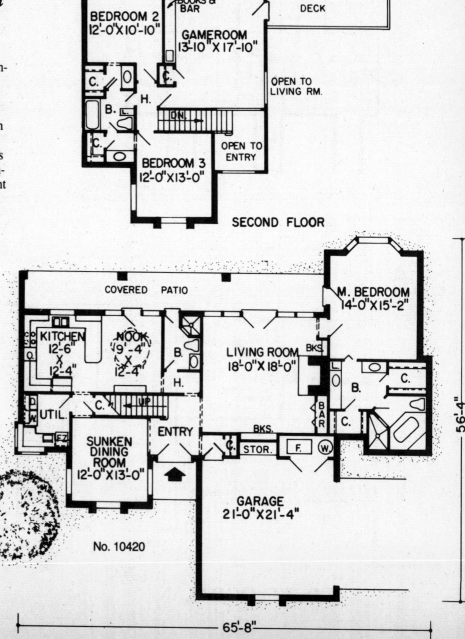

SECOND FLOOR

BEDROOM 2
12'-0"X10'-10"

BOOKS & BAR

DECK

GAMEROOM
13'-10" X 17'-10"

OPEN TO LIVING RM.

OPEN TO ENTRY

BEDROOM 3
12'-0"X13'-0"

COVERED PATIO

M. BEDROOM
14'-0"X15'-2"

KITCHEN
12'-6" X 12'-4"

NOOK
9'-4" X 12'-4"

LIVING ROOM
18'-0"X18'-0"

UTIL.

SUNKEN DINING ROOM
12'-0"X13'-0"

ENTRY

STOR.

GARAGE
21'-0"X21'-4"

56'-4"

65'-8"

No. 10420

Vaulted Ceiling and Balcony

No. 90308

The hallway leading between the bedrooms on the upper floor opens onto the floor below dramatizing the vaulted ceiling of the living room. Adjoining the living room is the dining room with its direct access to the centrally located kitchen. The breakfast nook along one side of the kitchen looks out over the deck. The family room, with its hearty fireplace and wet bar, completes the main floor of the home. The upper floor encompasses four bedrooms or three bedrooms and a den. The large master bedroom includes a five-piece bath, optional fireplace and a complete wall of closet space. Another bath is located just off the landing.

Total area — 2,460 sq. ft.

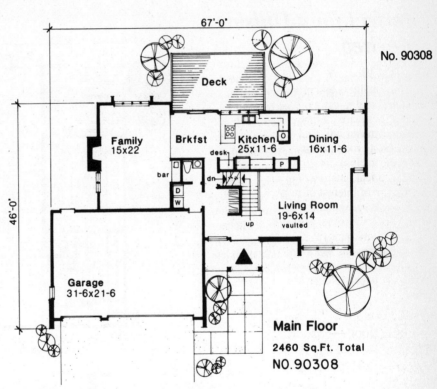

67'-0"

No. 90308

46'-0"

Deck

Family
15x22

Brkfst

Kitchen
25x11-6

Dining
16x11-6

bar

desk

D
W

dn

up

P

Living Room
19-6x14
vaulted

Garage
31-6x21-6

Main Floor

2460 Sq.Ft. Total
NO.90308

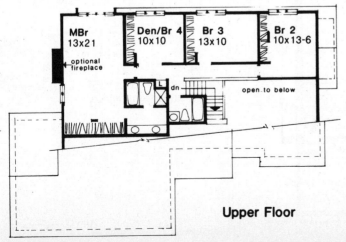

MBr
13x21

Den/Br 4
10x10

Br 3
13x10

Br 2
10x13-6

optional
fireplace

dn

open to below

Upper Floor

Perfect for a Hillside

No. 10595

From the road, the appearance of this two level home is deceiving. A central staircase directs traffic from the front entry to the den and master bedroom suite, to the living room, with its sloping ceiling and fireplace, or to the half bath, laundry and garage. Enter the island kitchen and formal dining room from either the breakfast or the living rooms. Two screened porches make outdoor living easy, rain or shine. Downstairs, the huge recreation room features a kitchenette and fireplace for entertaining. Two more bedrooms and a full bath complete this level, which could even be used for in-law quarters.

Upper floor — 1,643 sq. ft.
Lower floor — 1,297 sq. ft.
Garage — 528 sq. ft.

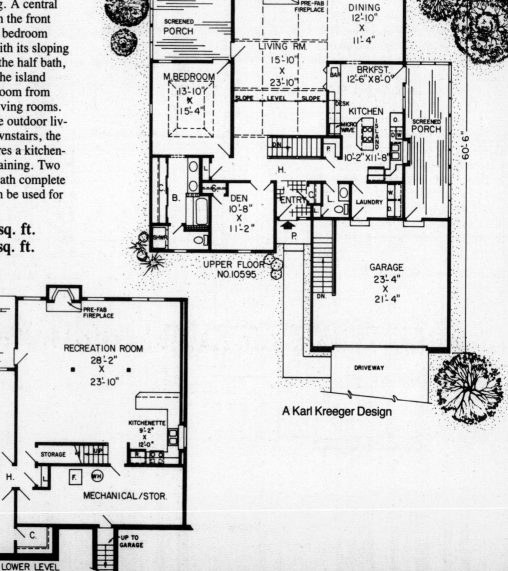

A Karl Kreeger Design

Energy-Saving Sunroom Warms Classic Tudor

First floor — 3,332 sq. ft.
Second floor — 1,218 sq. ft.
Sunroom — 340 sq. ft.
Basement — 3,672 sq. ft.
Garage — 1,137 sq. ft.

No. 10735

Here's a gracious family castle in a traditional style. From the dual-access curving stairway to the fireplaced living and family rooms with exposed beams, you'll find elegant touches everywhere. Look at the upstairs bedrooms with conveniently adjoining baths, the built-in bookshelves in the loft and study, and the angular bay windows and recessed ceilings in the dining room and master suite. But, this house isn't just beautiful. The island kitchen is designed for convenience. The sunroom saves your energy dollars by capturing heat in its tile floor. With a private hot tub and study, the first-floor master suite is a luxurious retreat for its lucky occupant.

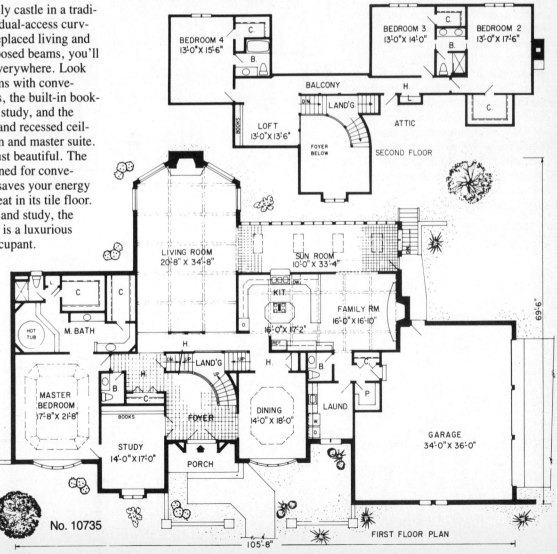

No. 10735

Oversized Windows
Let the Sun Shine In

No. 91024

Dramatic interior views characterize this three bedroom home. Walk through the double doors into the foyer, and you're greeted with a two-story panorama. On the entry level, you'll find the formal living room and bayed dining room. Step up to family living areas on the next level. The island kitchen, informal nook and the fireplaced family room are wide open for a sunny, warm atmosphere. Past the convenient utility areas and powder room, you'll find a quiet den with its own private deck. And, up the U-shaped central staircase, the bedroom level includes the master suite, complete with spa and private deck.

Main level — 1,843 sq. ft.
Upper level — 1,053 sq. ft.

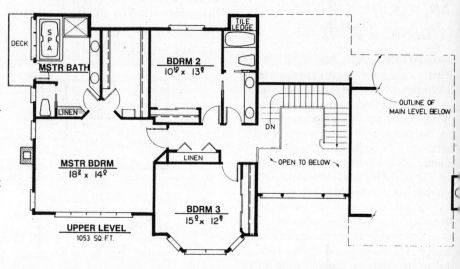

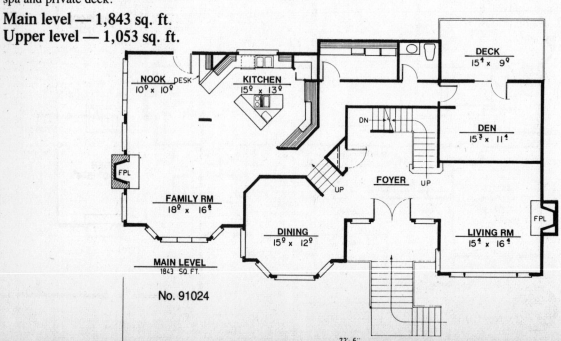

Master Bedroom, Den, Fill Second Level

No. 10332

A spacious master bedroom with double closets and adjoining bath is steps from the cozy den with a wood-burning fireplace on the upper level of this unique contemporary. Below, two additional bedrooms and living areas are grouped around a central hallway that allows access to the kitchen, bath or living and dining rooms. A garage and carport are featured.

First floor — 1,056 sq. ft.
Second floor — 736 sq. ft.
Basement — 1,056 sq. ft.
Garage — 668 sq. ft.

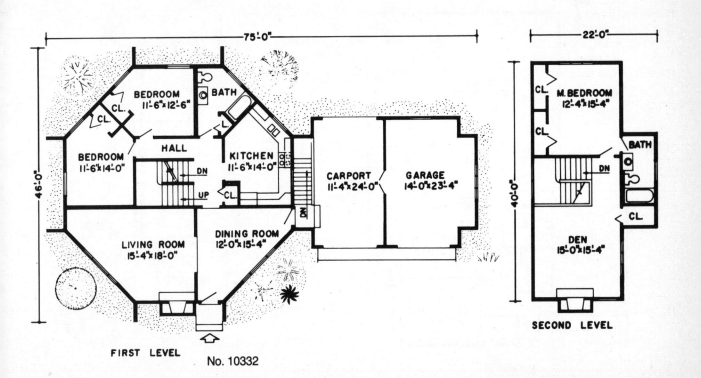

FIRST LEVEL

No. 10332

SECOND LEVEL

Two-Story Saltbox with Traditional Front

No. 1066

Brick veneer around the lower level of this two-story saltbox helps create its traditional front. Inside, areas of living are well zoned with the more active areas on the lower level and the quieter more private room on the second. A large utility room is located downstairs adjacent to the kitchen and is handy to the double garage and outdoors. Plenty of insulation throughout the design and a heat-circulating fireplace add to its energy efficiency.

First floor — 1,252 sq. ft.
Second floor — 766 sq. ft.
Garage — 489 sq. ft.

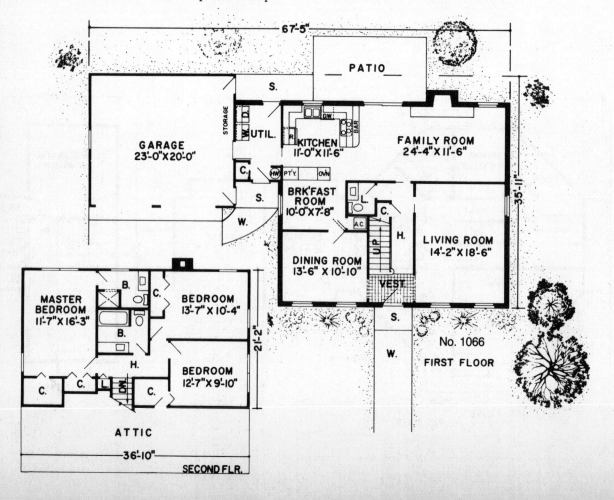

Multiple Peaks Add Intrigue

No. 10769

Here's a contemporary charmer with built-in convenience. Sloping ceilings and loads of windows give every sunny room a distinctive shape. And, with walk-in closets in every bedroom, a room-sized pantry off the kitchen, and extra storage throughout, you'll keep everything in its proper place. Active areas enjoy a wide-open feeling enhanced by a deck off the skylit dining room. Just around the corner, the first-floor master suite enjoys its own private sunbathing spot, along with a full bath that includes both walk-in shower and tub. The two bedrooms up the U-shaped staircase, which feature study nooks with a view, share a full bath with double vanities.

First floor — 1,578 sq. ft.
Second floor — 728 sq. ft.
Garage — 576 sq. ft.

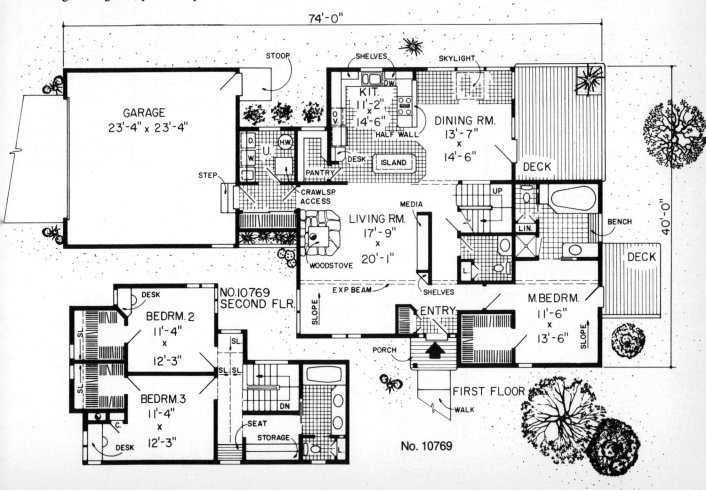

Large Covered Patio for Outdoor Enjoyment

No. 10436

Beauty and character flow from every area of this design. The double entry, set off by brickwork arches, ushers you into a large foyer with a curving staircase. The family room and fireplaced living room share a bar and with the patio, are sunken 12 inches lower than the adjoining rooms. On yet a third level are the utility room and garage which lie up 12 inches. In addition to the lower level master suite, three additional bedrooms are located upstairs and complete the sleeping accommodations. Each bedroom has direct access to a bath, and the largest of the three boasts a bay window and adjoining library.

First floor — 2,277 sq. ft.
Second floor — 851 sq. ft.
Garage — 493 sq. ft.

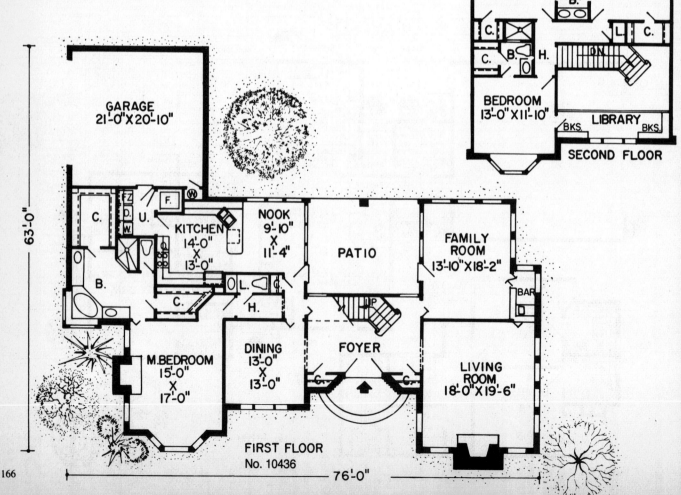

Contemporary Height

No. 10675

Vertical siding and stacked windows combine to create a soaring facade for this three-bedroom contemporary. Inside, sloping ceilings, bump out windows, and an open staircase unite the foyer, living room and formal dining room into one bright, airy space. The fireplaced family room and breakfast nook flanking the kitchen both open to an outdoor deck at the rear of the house. You'll find a full bath that serves two ample bedrooms right at the top of the stairs. And to the right, behind double doors, lies a luxurious master suite with skylit bath, walk-in closet, and double vanities.

First floor — 969 sq. ft.
Second floor — 714 sq. ft.
Basement — 969 sq. ft.
Garage — 484 sq. ft.

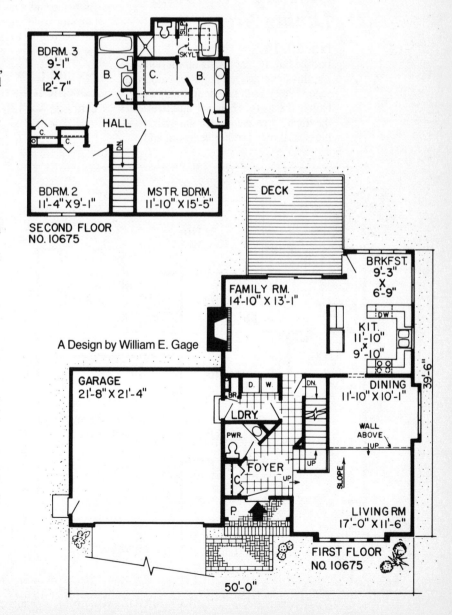

A Design by William E. Gage

Balcony Overlooks Dining Area

No. 10326

For the family that insists on individuality, this imaginative plan offers a partial second story with two bedrooms, a full bath and a 12 foot balcony that overlooks the dining area below. On the main level, the plan shows another bedroom and bath, a living room with wood-burning fireplace and a handy utility room. The corridor style kitchen borders a breakfast bar with entry to the large patio.

First floor — 1,146 sq. ft.
Second floor — 580 sq. ft.
Basement — 876 sq. ft.
Garage — 420 sq. ft.

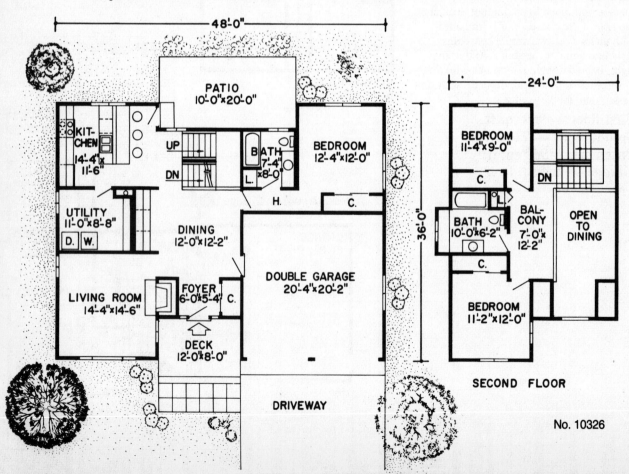

No. 10326

Rear of Home as Attractive as Front

No. 90413

The rear of this contemporary home features a massive stone fireplace and a full length deck which make it ideal for a mountain, golf course, lake, or other location where both the front and rear are visible. Sliding glass doors in the family room and breakfast nook open onto the deck. The modified A-Frame design combines a cathedral ceiling over the sunken family room with a large studio over the two front bedrooms. An isolated master suite features a walk-in closet and compartmentalized bath with double vanity and linen closet. The front bedrooms include ample closet space and share a unique bath-and-a-half arrangement. On one side of the U-shaped kitchen and

breakfast nook is the formal dining room which opens onto the foyer. On the other side is a utility room which can be entered from either the kitchen or garage. The exterior features a massive stone fireplace, large glass areas, and a combination of vertical wood siding and stone.

First floor — 2,192 sq. ft.
Second floor — 376 sq. ft.

FAMILY ROOM BELOW

DOWN

STOR

STUDIO
20·8 x 13·6

STOR

No. 90413

SECOND FLOOR

WOOD DECK

FAMILY ROOM
23-4 X 16-0

DINING ROOM
11-0 X 12-0

BREAKFAST
11-0 X 9-0

UTILITY

STORAGE

BATH

LINEN

DRESSING

DN.

BEDROOM
14-0 X 21-0

CLOSET

CLOS

DN.

UP

FOYER

PAN

KITCHEN
11 X 15

GARAGE
21-0 X 20-6

DRESS

BATH

DRESS

CLOSET

LIN

CLOSET

COATS

PORCH

44·8

BEDROOM
11-6 X 12-0

BEDROOM
11-6 X 12-0

91·2

Numerous Windows Light Lower Level Rooms

No. 10434

Soldier brickwork and graceful brick arches around 8 ft. living room windows immediately draw your attention. Other living room windows are all 6 feet high as are those of the nook and dining room. The master suite boasts a unique bath with large walk-in closet, separate shower and tub, and large angled lavatory. The second level study loft is open to the entry below and provides two unbroken walls for books if you desire. Two additional bedrooms on this level share a full bath; both bedrooms with large closets and one with a 6 ft. dormer window. Natural light from a skylight looks in on the stairway.

First floor — 1,604 sq. ft.
Second floor — 594 sq. ft.
Garage — 502 sq. ft.
Covered porch — 48 sq. ft.

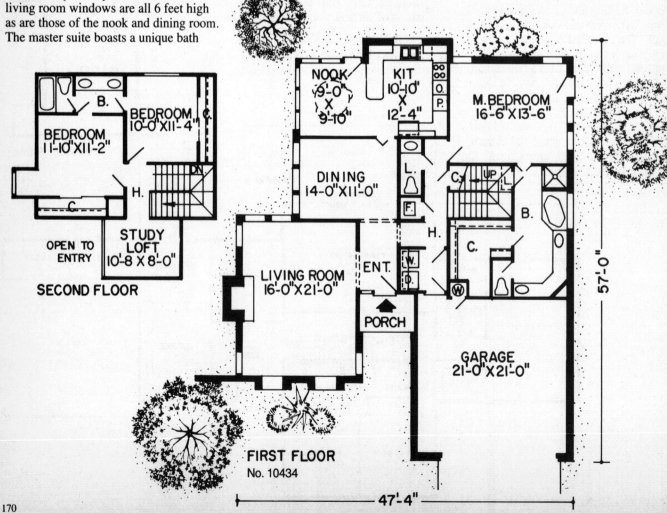

SECOND FLOOR

FIRST FLOOR
No. 10434

Design Incorporates Informal and Formal

No. 90317

The main level of this two-story home is divided into formal and informal living areas by the central placement of the staircase and the kitchen. The two-story living room and the dining room with its unique bump-out window are located to one side of the home. On the other side are the family room with its inviting fireplace and the breakfast room which has sliding glass doors onto the deck. Four bedrooms comprise the second floor. The expansive master bedroom features a five-piece bath and two walk-in closets.

Main level — 1,371 sq. ft.
Upper level — 666 sq. ft.
Basement — 1,413 sq. ft.
Garage — 484 sq. ft.

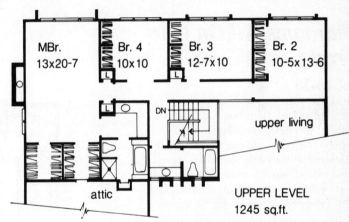

MBr. 13x20-7   Br. 4 10x10   Br. 3 12-7x10   Br. 2 10-5x13-6

DN

upper living

attic

UPPER LEVEL
1245 sq.ft.

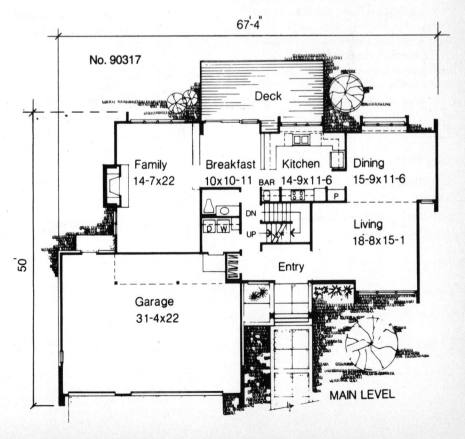

67'-4"

No. 90317

Deck

Family 14-7x22   Breakfast 10x10-11   Kitchen 14-9x11-6   BAR   Dining 15-9x11-6

DN   P

UP   Living 18-8x15-1

50'

D W

Entry

Garage 31-4x22

MAIN LEVEL

Bedrooms All On One Level

No. 10430

If you like your bedrooms all on one level, but still prefer privacy for the master suite, this design will suit those desires. The noise and merriment usually associated with a game room have been zoned away from the more formal living areas by locating this room on the second level. Game room and master bedroom suite share a deck. Featuring three living levels on the first floor, the dining room is situated down two steps and the dining room down one step from other areas. Traffic is easily funneled through the brick arched angled front entry or garage-utility entrance to a central hallway and stairs, which helps guest, family members, groceries, etc. get where they are going with fewer steps and less congestion.

First floor — 1,355 sq. ft.
Second floor — 1,426 sq. ft.
Garage — 517 sq. ft.
Covered areas — 194 sq. ft.

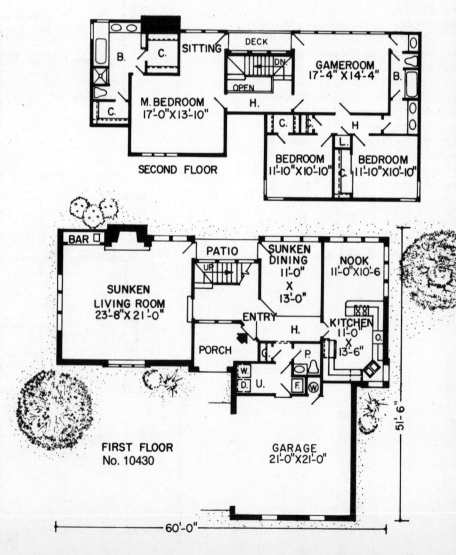

Enticing Angles

No. 26500

From every angle this two-story house has a special allure. Thrusting roofiness echoed in the siding pattern creates an exciting exterior. Entrance to this unique home is gained through an air-lock-garden assuring privacy and comfort. Interior pleasures include a magnificent great room and sunken conversation area with a fireplace. Sliding glass doors from the great room open onto a large patio. Slightly elevated are the kitchen, dining room and breakfast room with bay windows. The master bedroom upstairs has a private deck.

First floor — 1,818 sq. ft.
Second floor — 484 sq. ft.
Basement — 530 sq. ft.
Garage — 797 sq. ft.

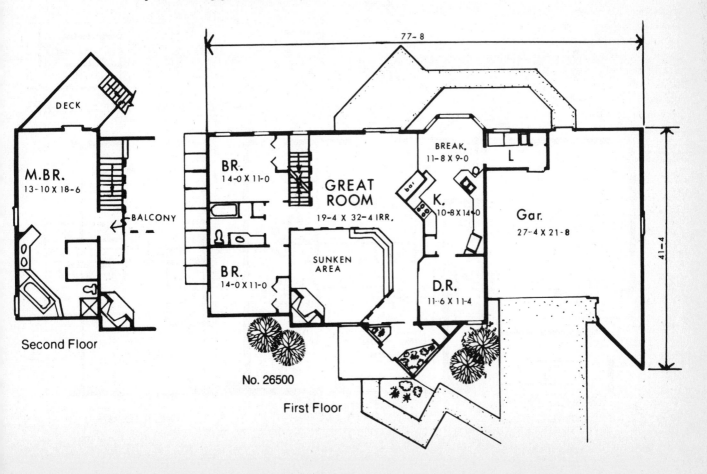

Second Floor

No. 26500

First Floor

Move in Today, Finish it Later

No. 9115

This unusual but quite attractive story and one-half home features a spiral stairway to the second floor. An alternative is shown for those that prefer a more convenient stairway. The three bedrooms on the upper level could be left unfinished by the contractor and then finished by the man of the house during his leisure hours. The family room would serve as the master bedroom in this case. The kitchen area is quite nice with an abundance of cabinets, a separate laundry and a large breakfast nook.

First floor — 1,185 sq. ft.
Second floor — 549 sq. ft.
Garage — 484 sq.ft.

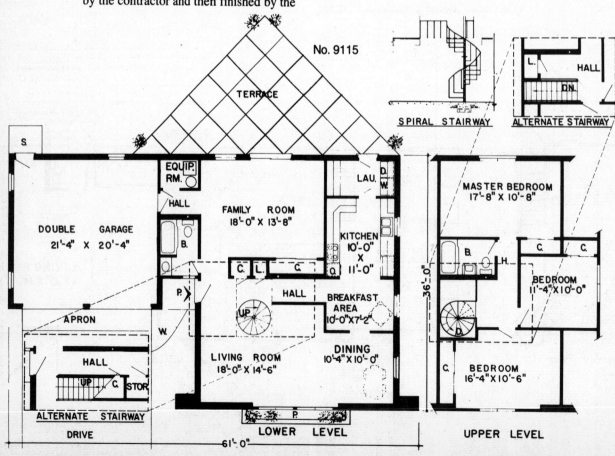

No. 9115

SPIRAL STAIRWAY   ALTERNATE STAIRWAY

TERRACE

EQUIP. RM.

HALL

DOUBLE GARAGE
21'-4" X 20'-4"

FAMILY ROOM
18'-0" X 13'-8"

LAU.

D.W.

KITCHEN
10'-0" X 11'-0"

MASTER BEDROOM
17'-8" X 10'-8"

B.

C.

L.

C.

HALL

BREAKFAST AREA
10'-0"X7'-2"

B.

H.

C.   C.

BEDROOM
11'-4"X10'-0"

APRON

UP

W.

P.

36'-0"

HALL

UP   STOR

C.

LIVING ROOM
18'-0" X 14'-6"

DINING
10'-4"X10'-0"

D.

C.

BEDROOM
16'-4"X10'-6"

ALTERNATE STAIRWAY

DRIVE

P.

LOWER LEVEL

UPPER LEVEL

61'-0"

Energy Saving
Envelope Design

No. 10378

Double walls on the north and south sides of this design provide an envelope for the passage of warm air generated in the greenhouse and solar panels on the roof and sidewalls. Rooms are thus warmed by heat radiated from the envelope space (plenum). In addition, water tubes in an insulated basement space absorb heat during the day to be released at night or on cloudy days. 12″ of attic insulation guards against heat loss and 2 x 6 studs with 6″ of R-19 insulation are shown for sidewalls.

First floor — 960 sq. ft.
Second floor — 960 sq. ft.
Basement — 960 sq. ft.
Garage — 576 sq. ft.
Greenhouse — 120 sq. ft.
Deck — 200 sq. ft.

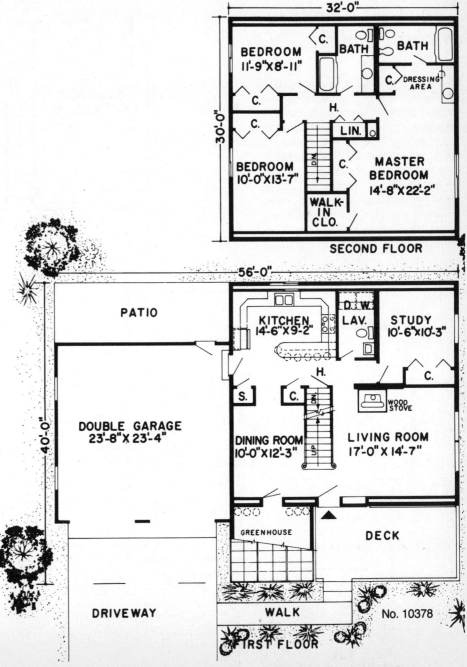

Cape Cod Adapts to Modern Living

No. 9098

Charmingly traditional in appearance, this Cape Cod design incorporates four sizable bedrooms, a compartmented bath, and a terrace, among other features that make this a highly livable plan. The efficient kitchen outlines a breakfast nook overlooking the terrace, and the living room enjoys a fireplace and adjoins the separate dining room. Dormer windows add interest to the upstairs bedrooms which are spacious and well furnished with closet space.

Main floor — 1,142 sq. ft.
Second floor — 900 sq. ft.
Garage — 480 sq. ft.
Porch — 96 sq. ft.

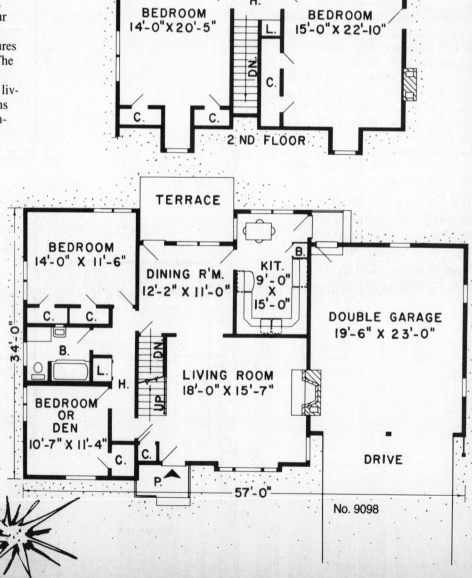

Tudor Plan Annexes Roofed Porch

No. 10006

Contrasting stone and stucco slashed with rough timbers give character to this English Tudor plan, extended on two sides by a roofed porch. Rooms are proportioned for efficiency, especially the second floor bath complex, segmented to allow maximum use. Taking command in the living room is a warm wood-burning fireplace, and the attached dining room is furnished with sliding glass doors to the porch area. A built-in dressing table benefits the master bedroom, which also includes a full bath and double closets.

First floor — 1,926 sq. ft.
Second floor — 864 sq. ft.
Garage — 583 sq. ft.
Basement — 1,926 sq. ft.

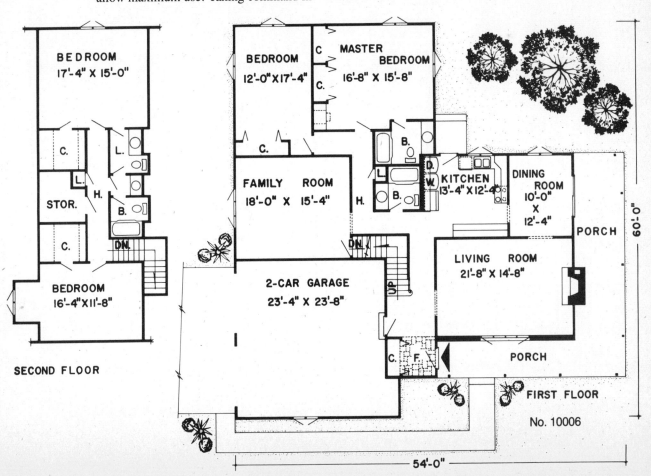

SECOND FLOOR

FIRST FLOOR

No. 10006

Cape Cod Passive Solar Design

No. 10386

Here is a traditional Cape Cod design made practical by numerous passive solar features. A solar greenhouse on the south employs energy storage rods and water to capture the sun's warmth, thereby providing a sanctuary for plants and supplying a good percentage of the house's heat. Other southern windows are large and triple glazed for energy efficiency. Two bedrooms and a bath are located on the second floor. From one of the bedrooms you can look out through louvered shutters to the living room below, accented by a heat circulating fireplace and a cathedral ceiling with three dormer windows which flood the room with light. On the lower level, sliding glass doors lead from the sitting area of the master bedroom suite to a private patio.

Also on this level are a dining room, kitchen, mud room, double garage with a large storage area and another larger patio.

First floor — 1,164 sq. ft.
Second floor — 574 sq. ft.
Basement — 1,164 sq. ft.
Greenhouse — 238 sq. ft.
Garage & storage — 566 sq. ft.

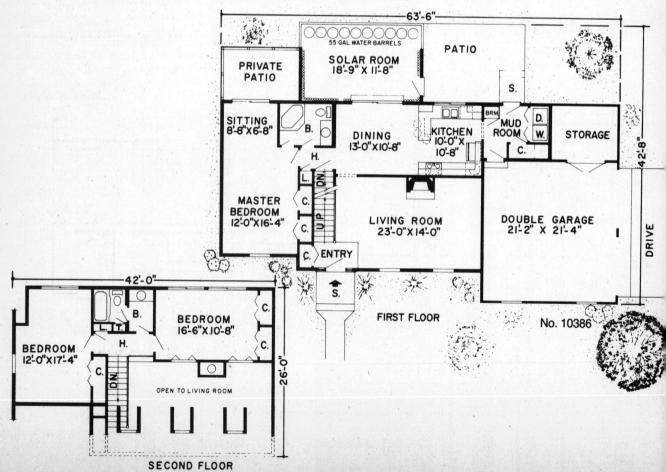

Varied Roofline Features Modern Amenities

No. 90156

The spacious foyer allows easy traffic flow to all areas of the home. The sunken living room has a sloped roof to the second floor balcony library. A two-way fireplace opens to both the living and family rooms. The kitchen provides abundant counter space, pantry and wetbar. The master suite offers a dressing area, walk-in closet and deluxe bath with the added feature of a balcony library overlooking the living room. Three additional bedrooms and a bath complete the second floor.

**First floor — 1,432 sq. ft.
Second floor — 1,319 sq. ft.**

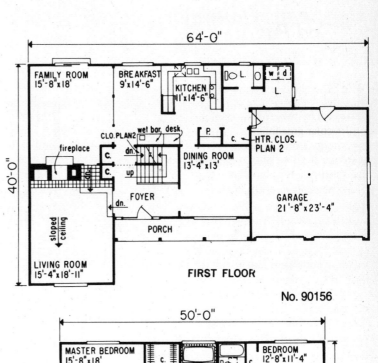

FIRST FLOOR

No. 90156

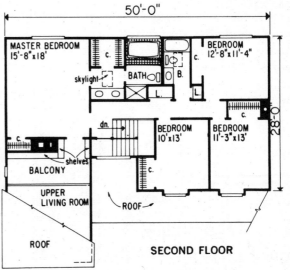

SECOND FLOOR

Bridge Spans Hallway

No. 10426

The splendor and luxury of this home give way to a functional and practical floor plan. The cloistered entry immediately introduces guests to an impressive central hallway, rising to four skylights high above. Lightened by two stories of glass and decorated by exposed exterior rafter beams, stairs on the left connect to upper level rooms on the right via a bridge which spans the entry hallway. The master suite includes a fireplace sitting area, a large walk-through closet and a windowed bath area, sheltered by a brick privacy fence. A bar, fireplace and full length windows are featured in the spacious 25 x 26 living room. Double doors exit the formal dining room to a covered side porch. Perfect for a southern exposure, the sun soaking solarium lends heat and natural light to four adjacent rooms.

First floor — 2,004 sq. ft.
Second floor — 591 sq. ft.
Solarium — 240 sq. ft.

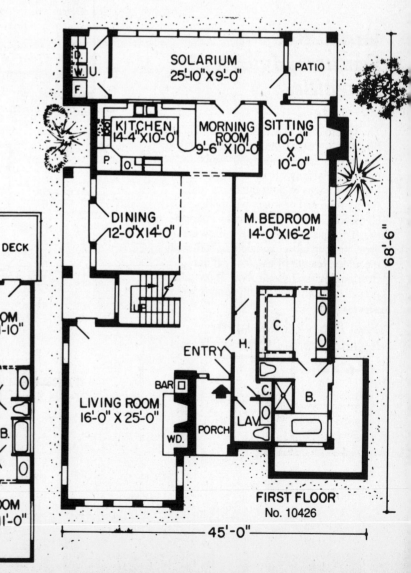

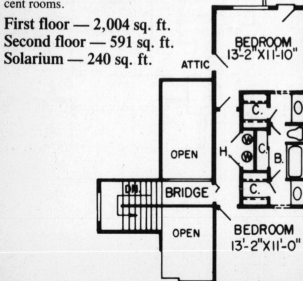

Lots of Living Space in this Four-Bedroom Starter

No. 10491

Put the kids in the three upstairs bedrooms and enjoy the privacy afforded by the first floor master suite. The upstairs bath is designed with the family in mind; it is over-sized, compartmentalized and has a basin in each of the compartments. The first floor master suite has a full wall of closet space and a private entrance to the bath. The rest of the first floor is composed of integrated living areas. The family room blends with the dining area and is separated from the galley kitchen by a preparation center. This compact plan is ideally suited to a site with a narrow lot line.

First floor — 1,012 sq. ft.
Second floor — 623 sq. ft.
Garage — 550 sq. ft.

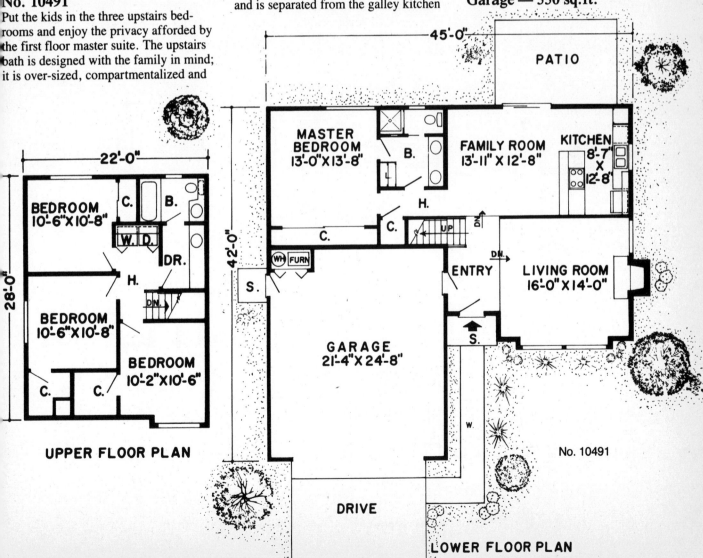

UPPER FLOOR PLAN

LOWER FLOOR PLAN

No. 10491

Two-Way Fireplace Warms Living Areas

No. 10652

Stucco, fieldstone, and rough-hewn timbers grace the elegant exterior of this three-bedroom family home. But with abundant windows, high ceilings, and an open plan, this cheerful abode is a far cry from the chilly tudor castle of long ago.

Flanked by a vaulted formal dining room and a stairway to the upstairs bedrooms, full bath, and built-in cedar closet, the central foyer leads to a spacious living room, kept comfortable in any season by a ceiling fan. Nearby, the first-floor master suite is loaded with amenities: a walk-in closet, skylit double vanities, and a sunken tub. Notice the cooktop island convenience in the kitchen, the built-in

bar adjacent to the living room, and the rear deck accessible through french doors in the breakfast room.

First floor — 1,789 sq. ft.
Second floor — 568 sq. ft.
Basement — 1,789 sq. ft.
Garage — 529 sq. ft.

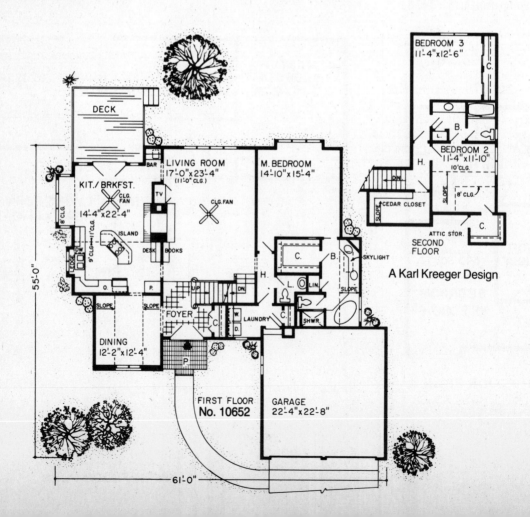

A Karl Kreeger Design

Tradition with a Twist

No. 90933

A traditional exterior hides a multitude of special features that distinguishes this attractive four-bedroom abode. The inviting porch leads into the central foyer, illuminated by a skylight far overhead. You'll find the living and formal dining rooms adjacent to the entry, with informal family areas grouped conveniently at the rear of the house. Separated from the breakfast nook only by a railing, the sunken family room is warmed by a fireplace. Upstairs, the master suite boasts an added attraction — a hidden sundeck, tucked behind the garage for privacy.

First floor — 1,104 sq. ft.
Second floor — 845 sq. ft.

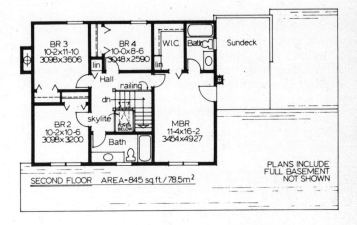

SECOND FLOOR   AREA=845 sq.ft./78.5m²

PLANS INCLUDE
FULL BASEMENT
NOT SHOWN

No. 90933

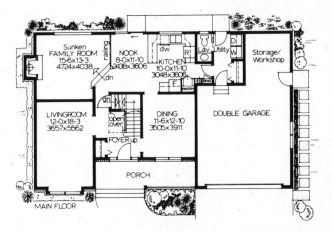

MAIN FLOOR

Double Decks Adorn Luxurious Master Suite

No. 91022

Curves soften the exterior and interior spaces of this dramatic contemporary designed for sun worshippers. Abundant windows, indoor planters and three decks unite every room with the great outdoors. Steps and railings divide active areas without compromising the home's airy feeling. When the sun goes down, enjoy the warmth of the fireplace in the living and dining rooms or the wood stove in the family room. Main floor bedrooms, adjacent to a convenient full bath, are tucked away from family areas for quiet bedtimes. And, the master suite upstairs is a wonderful retreat you're sure to enjoy.

Main floor — 1,985 sq. ft.
Upper floor — 715 sq. ft.

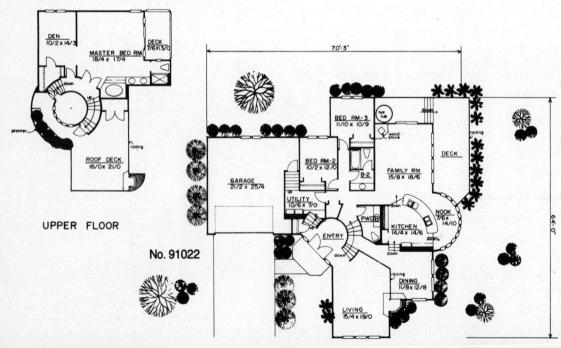

UPPER FLOOR

No. 91022

MAIN FLOOR

Perfect For Entertaining

No. 20050

As guests enter the two-story, tiled foyer, they are immediately welcomed by the expansive living room with its sloped ceiling and cheery fireplace. Lead them into the dining room and serve them from the adjacent kitchen. There's even room for more than one cook in this roomy kitchen which opens onto a covered deck for outdoor meals. The first floor master bedroom features a large, five-piece bath and double closets. Upstairs are two more bedrooms with roomy closets, an additional bath and room for storage in the attic.

First floor — 1,303 sq. ft.
Second floor — 596 sq. ft.
Basement — 1,303 sq. ft.
Garage — 460 sq. ft.

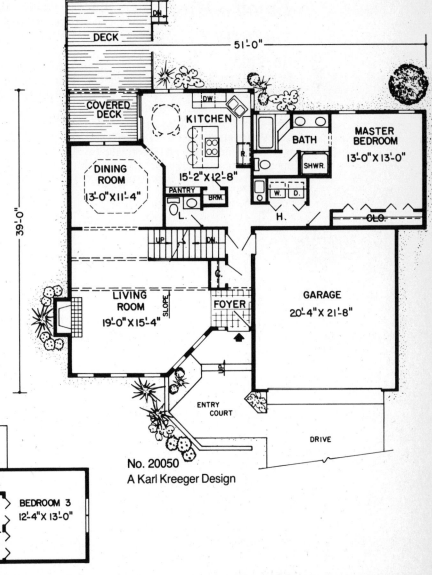

DECK

51'-0"

COVERED DECK

KITCHEN
15'-2" X 12'-8"

DW

BATH

MASTER BEDROOM
13'-0" X 13'-0"

DINING ROOM
13'-0" X 11'-4"

39'-0"

PANTRY

BRM.

SHWR.

W. D.

L.

H.

CLO.

UP   DN

LIVING ROOM
19'-0" X 15'-4"

SLOPE

FOYER

GARAGE
20'-4" X 21'-8"

UP

ENTRY COURT

DRIVE

No. 20050
A Karl Kreeger Design

BEDROOM 2
11'-6" X 13'-0"

SLP.

CLO.

ATTIC STORAGE

H.

DN

B.

BEDROOM 3
12'-4" X 13'-0"

C.

SLOPE

LIVING ROOM BELOW

BALCONY

FOYER BELOW

SECOND FLOOR
NO. 20050

Enjoy a Hint of Victorian Charm

No. 91001

Stepping through the curved brick archway of this contemporary gem, you'll encounter a spacious, two-story entry flooded with light. The open feeling continues throughout the main floor. Glass walls unite the formal and informal dining and fireplaced family rooms with your back yard. The convenient kitchen mirrors the angles in the bay-windowed breakfast nook, creating interesting angles in every room. Upstairs, enjoy quiet hours behind the double doors of the study, or in the luxurious master suite.

Total area — 2,176 sq. ft.

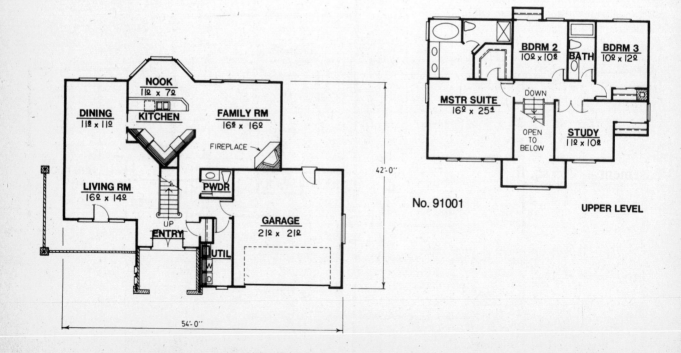

Dignified Design Opens to Family Style Floor Plan

No. 10496

Four spacious bedrooms are arranged on the upper level of this plan so that privacy is maintained without any wasted space. Two of the bedrooms share a bath while the other two large bedrooms each have a private bath and a walk-in closet. The living space on the lower level is highlighted by a spacious family room with a beamed ceiling, fireplace, bookcases, wetbar and direct access to both the patio and informal dining nook. The more formal dining room and living room are located on the other side of the well-designed U-shaped kitchen. The double garage even has plenty of room for a workshop and extra bicycles.

Lower level — 1,330 sq. ft.
Upper level — 1,301 sq. ft.
Garage — 610 sq. ft.
Basement — 765 sq. ft.

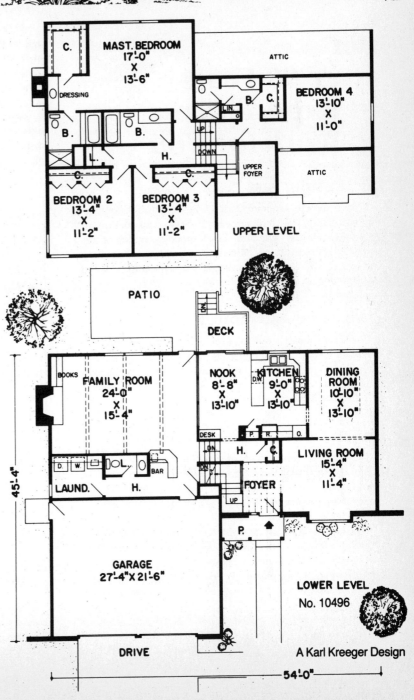

A Karl Kreeger Design

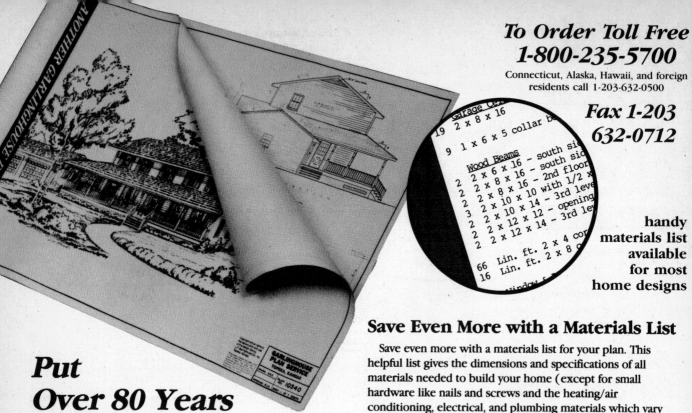

Put Over 80 Years of Experience to Work for You

Get Results Fast

Your complete, accurate Garlinghouse blueprints contain all the information your builder needs to begin construction on your custom home right away. You'll speed every step of the construction of your new home because each detail of construction and materials is already worked out for you and your builder.

Save Time and Money

There's no cheaper way to have the home you've always wanted than our custom blueprints. You pay only a fraction of the original design cost by a respected architect or professional designer. And, our years of experience go into every plan to save you costly mistakes and delays during construction.

Speed Construction, Avoid Delay

You'll speed every step of construction by ordering enough sets of blueprints for the job. Experience shows that 8 sets is best. Once you begin building, everyone seems to need a set. Your lending institution, local building authority, and general contractor each need a set.

And, of course, all the subcontractors will need a set once work is underway . . . the foundation contractor, the framing carpenters, the plumbing contractor, the heating and air conditioning contractor, the electrical contractor, the insulation contractor, the drywall or plastering contractor, the finish carpenters, etc.

While some sets can be handed down as work progresses, you'll avoid delays by having enough sets and eliminate worry about sets being lost or ruined on the job. You'll get faster and better results with the standard 8-set construction package.

Save Even More with a Materials List

Save even more with a materials list for your plan. This helpful list gives the dimensions and specifications of all materials needed to build your home (except for small hardware like nails and screws and the heating/air conditioning, electrical, and plumbing materials which vary according to your local building codes).

With this valuable list, you'll get faster and more accurate bids from your suppliers and avoid paying for unnecessary materials and waste. A materials list is available for most of our plans. Ask when you order.

Here's What You Get

Every set of our complete, accurate blueprints contains everything you need to begin building:

- *Front, rear, and both side views of the house (elevations)*
- *Floor plans for all levels*
- *Foundation plan*
- *Roof plan*
- *Typical wall sections (cross sectional slices through the home)*
- *Kitchen and bathroom cabinet details*
- *Fireplace details (where applicable)*
- *Stair details (where applicable)*
- *Plot plan*
- *Locations of electrical fixtures and components*
- *Specifications and contract form*
- *Energy Conservation Specifications Guide*
- *Complete materials list (only if ordered and available)*

Add a Personal Touch to Your Home

Your custom dream home can be as wonderful as you want. Easy modifications, such as minor non-structural changes and simple building material substitutions, can be made by any competent builder without the need for blueprint revisions. However, if you are considering making major changes to your design, we strongly recommend that you seek the services of an architect or professional designer. Even these expensive professional services will cost less with our complete, detailed plans as a starting point.

Our Custom Design Staff may be able to help you, too, for a very reasonable hourly charge. One advantage of choosing our staff is that we make changes directly to our original drawings and give you a new, complete set of blueprints. Other architects can only attach modified drawings to our originals, which can be more confusing and time consuming for your builder. Call us for more information. Please note that we can make no modifications to #90,000 series plans.

Discover Reverse Plans

You may find that a particular house would suit your taste or fit your lot better if it were "reversed." A reverse plan turns the design end-for-end. That is, if the garage is shown on the left side and the bedrooms on the right, the reverse plan will place the garage on the right side and the bedrooms on the left. To see quickly how a design will look in reverse, hold your book in front of a mirror.

The dimensions and lettering for some Garlinghouse reverse plans are corrected to be right reading on the reversed plan. When this is not the case, one mirror image, reversed set (with "backwards" lettering and dimensions) is provided as a master guide for you and your builder. The remaining sets are then sent as shown in our catalog for ease in reading the lettering and dimensions and marked "REVERSE" with a special stamp to eliminate confusion. (Available only on multiple set orders.)

Prices are effective 1988 and subject to change without notice.

Price Schedule

One Complete Set of Blueprints	$125.00
Minimum Construction Package (5 sets)	$170.00
Standard Construction Package (8 sets)	$200.00
Each Additional Set Ordered With One of the Above Packages	$20.00
Materials List (with plan order only)	$15.00

Builders: ask about our reproducible sepia mylars for professional use. Prices range from $340 to $475. Note that plans numbered 90,000 and above are not available. Call 203-632-0500 for more information and to order.

Important Shipping Information

We process and ship your order within 72 hours of receipt, usually via UPS. Then, it normally takes another 5 to 7 working days for delivery. Please allow 10 working days for delivery from the time we receive your order.

Note that UPS will deliver only to street addresses and rural route delivery boxes and not to Post Office Box numbers. Please print your complete street address. If no one is home during the day, you may use your work address to insure prompt delivery.

We **MUST** ship First Class Mail to Alaska or Hawaii, APO, FPO, or a Post Office box. Please note the higher cost for First Class Mail.

Domestic Shipping	
UPS Ground Service	$5.75
First Class Mail	$7.75

For fastest service, use your **Visa or Mastercard** and call our Toll Free number. If you are in a special hurry, we offer ultra-fast delivery for an additional charge. Ask for details when you place your order.

International Orders and Shipping

If you are ordering from outside the United States, please note that your check, money order, or international money transfer **must be payable in U.S. currency.**

Also note that due to the extremely long delays involved with surface mail, we ship all international orders via Air Parcel Post. Please refer to the schedule below for the mailing charge on your order and substitute this amount instead of the usual mailing charge for domestic orders.

International Shipping	One set	Multiple sets
Canada	$ 5.75	$ 9.75
Mexico & Caribbean nations	$16.50	$39.50
All other nations	$18.50	$50.00

for fastest service . . .
Order Toll Free
1-800-235-5700
Connecticut, Alaska, Hawaii, and foreign residents call 1-203-632-0500
Please have your credit card and order form ready when you call
Fax 1-203-632-0712

The Garlinghouse Co., P.O. Box 1717, Middletown, CT 06457

Blueprint Order Form

Please send me: code no. 20020

☐ One Complete Set of Blueprints ($125.00)
☐ Minimum Construction Package: five sets ($170.00)
☐ Standard Construction Package: eight sets ($200.00)

Plan no. _____ ☐ as shown ☐ reversed

Cost of Blueprints . . . .$ _____
_____ Additional Set(s) $20.00 each . . . . .$ _____
          with original order
Materials List ($15.00 per order) . . . .$ _____
Shipping Charges (see charts) . . . .$ _____
Tax* . . . .$ _____
      *Kansas Residents Add 5% Sales Tax
       Connecticut Residents Add 7.5% Sales Tax
Total Amount Enclosed . . . .$ [   ]

Purchaser hereby agrees that the home plan construction drawings being purchased will not be used for the construction of more than one single dwelling, and that these drawings will not be reproduced, either in whole or in part, by any means whatsoever.

Charge my Order to: ☐ Mastercard   ☐ Visa

Card No. [   ]

Exp.
Date _____ Signature _____

Name _____
                        (please print)

Address _____

City & State _____ Zip _____

Daytime Telephone No. (_____) _____

Send your Check or Money Order to:
The Garlinghouse Company
34 Industrial Park Place, P.O. Box 1717
Middletown, Connecticut 06457

Builder's Library

The books on this page were written with the professional home builder in mind. They are all comprehensive information sources for contractors or for those beginners who wish to build like contractors.

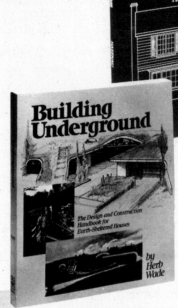

◄ **2518. Build Your Own Home** An authoritative guide on how to be your own general contractor. This book goes through the step-by-step process of building a house with special emphasis on the business aspects such as financing, scheduling, permits, insurance, and more. Furthermore, it gives you an understanding of what to expect out of your various subcontractors so that you can properly orchestrate their work. 112 pp.; Holland House (paperback) **$12.95**

▶ **2600. Building Underground** This has been compiled on earth sheltered homes, built all over North America—homes that are spacious, attractive and comfortable in every way. These homes are more energy efficient than above ground houses. Physical security, low operating costs, and noise reduction further enhance their attractiveness. 304 pp.; 85 photos; 112 illus.; Rodale Press (paperback) **$14.95**

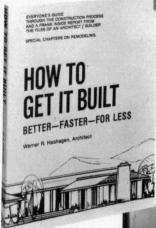

◄ **2596. How To Get It Built** No matter how small or how large your construction project is, building will be easier with this informative guidebook. This text was prepared for people involved in building on a non-professional basis. Guidelines have been carefully prepared to follow step-by-step construction-cost savings methods. Written by an architect/contractor, this book offers home construction owners the planning, construction and cost saving solutions to his own building needs. 238 pp.; over 300 illus.; (paperback) Hashagen **$18.00**

from the Leading Publishers in the Do-It-Yourself Industry!!!

▶ **2508. Modern Plumbing** All aspects of plumbing installation, service, and repair are presented here in illustrated, easy-to-follow text. This book contains all the information needed for vocational competence, including the most up-to-date tools, materials, and practices. 300 pp.; over 700 illus.; Goodheart-Willcox (hardcover) **$17.60**

▲ **2607. Radon: The Invisible Threat** This book will help you become more aware of this potentially harmful situation, with easy, step-by-step instructions, to help you detect the presence of Radon Gas in your home. Also included is a simple test that could prevent your home from becoming a victim of this environmental hazard. 224 pp.; Rodale (paperback) **$12.95**

▲ **2546. Blueprint Reading for Construction** This combination text and workbook shows and tells how to read residential, commercial, and light industrial prints. With an abundance of actual drawings from industry, you learn step by step about each component of a set of blueprints, including even cost estimating. 336 pp.; Goodheart-Willcox (spiral bound) **$18.40**

▲ **2570. Modern Masonry** Everything you will ever need to know about concrete, masonry, and brick, is included in this book. Forms construction, concrete reinforcement, proper foundation construction, and bricklaying are among the topics covered in step-by-step detail. An excellent all-round reference and guide. 256 pp.; 700 illus.; Goodheart-Willcox (hardcover) **$17.00**

▼ **2514. The Underground House Book** For anyone seriously interested in building and living in an underground home, this book tells it all. Aesthetic considerations, building codes, site planning, financing, insurance, planning and decorating considerations, maintenance costs, soil, excavation, landscaping, water considerations, humidity control, and specific case histories are among the many facets of underground living dealt with in this publication. 208 pp.; 140 illus.; Garden Way (paperback) **$10.95**

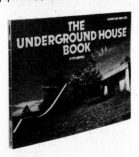

▼ **2504. Architecture, Residential Drawing and Design** An excellent text that explains all the fundamentals on how to create a complete set of construction drawings. Specific areas covered include proper design and planning considerations, foundation plans, floor plans, elevations, stairway details, electrical plans, plumbing plans, etc. 492 pp.; over 800 illus.; Goodheart-Willcox (hardcover) **$22.00**

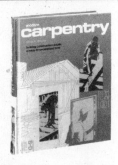

▲ **2510. Modern Carpentry** A complete guide to the "nuts and bolts" of building a home. This book explains all about building materials, framing, trim work, insulation, foundations, and much more. A valuable text and reference guide. 492 pp.; over 1400 illus.; Goodheart-Willcox (hardcover) **$22.00**

▲ **2506. House Wiring Simplified** This book teaches all the fundamentals of modern house wiring; shows how it's done with easy-to-understand drawings. A thorough guide to the materials and practices for safe, efficient installation of home electrical systems. 176 pp.; 384 illus.; Goodheart-Willcox (hardcover) **$9.20**

▼ **2544. Solar Houses** An examination of solar homes from the standpoint of lifestyle. This publication shows you through photographs, interviews, and practical information, what a solar lifestyle involves, how owners react to it, and what the bottom-line economics are. Included are 130 floor plans and diagrams which give you a clear idea of how various "active" and "passive" solar systems work. 160 pp.; 370 illus. Pantheon (paperback) **$9.95**

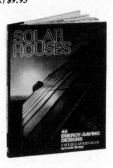

▼ **2592. How to Design & Build Decks & Patios** Learn how to create decks and patios to suit every type of lot and lifestyle. This fully illustrated source book includes detailed information on design and construction as well as special charts on building and paving materials. Full color, 112 pp.; Ortho (paperback) **$6.95**

▲ **2609. Kitchens** Gather your family around you in your new kitchen, with tips from the professionals in the industry, as well as 105 color photos to help you design your new kitchen. With recommendations on a wide variety of related topics, even the casual reader is sure to find exciting new ideas for their kitchen. 160 pp.; Rodale (paperback) **$12.95**

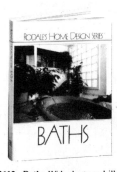

▲ **2612. Baths** With charts and illustrations provided, BATHS gives tips on new storage ideas, suggestions on whirlpools and saunas, and a tour of 30 of the best-designed baths in the United States. Assistance is provided in the form of addresses of leading manufacturers and helpful organizations, to aid you in the remodeling of your bath. 154 pp.; Rodale (paperback) **$12.95**

▼ **2611. Tile It Up! Plumb It Up!** Using the many illustrations and the easy steps included in this valuable book, you will be able to work just like the professionals. This book provides step-by-step instructions on plumbing and tiling, enabling the do-it-yourselfer to complete these projects with a minimum of time providing maximum results. 43 pp.; XS Books (paperback) **$6.95**

▼ **2516. Building Consultant** The new home buyer's bible to home construction. This encyclopedia of home building explains in comprehensive detail about all the various elements that go into a completed house. It enables you to deal with the construction of your new home in a meaningful way that will avoid costly errors, whether you use a contractor or build it yourself. 188 pp.; Holland House (paperback) **$12.95**

Builder's Library order form

Yes! send me the following books:

book order no.	price
_____	$ _____
_____	$ _____
_____	$ _____
_____	$ _____
_____	$ _____
_____	$ _____

Postage & handling (one book only) $ 1.75

Add 50¢ postage & handling
    for each additional book $ _____

Canada add $1.50 per book $ _____

Resident sales tax: Kansas (5%) $ _____

            Connecticut (7.5%)

      TOTAL ENCLOSED $ _____

No C.O.D. orders accepted; U.S. funds only.
prices subject to change without notice

My Shipping Address is:
(please print)

Name _____

Address _____

City _____

State _____ Zip _____

Send your order to:
(With check or money order enclosed)

**The Garlinghouse Company
34 Industrial Park Place
P.O. Box 1717
Middletown, Connecticut 06457**

For Faster Service . . .
CHARGE IT!   (203) 632-0500

☐ MasterCard   ☐ Visa

Card # |__|__|__|__|__|__|__|__|__|__|__| Exp. Date _____

Signature _____

192

▼ **2604. The Low Maintenance House**
At last, an idea-packed book that will save you thousands of hours on home maintenance. It's an essential planning guide for anyone building a home. Discover new as well as time-tested techniques and products for cutting down the time, and slashing the money you spend to clean and repair your home . . . from roof to basement, from front yard to backyard garden. This book will earn its price, and your thanks, over and over again. 314 pp.; Rodale (hardback) **$19.95**

▲ **2605. Contracting Your Home** With over 150 illustrations, this guide offers many suggestions and ideas on contracting your own home. Many forms you can copy and re-use are provided, giving checklists and a glossary of terms used by the professionals, as well as all the necessary estimating forms. 279 pp.; Betterway Publications (paperback) **$18.95**

▼ **2608. Cut Your Electric Bill in Half**
With assistance from this book, you may be able to cut your future electric bills by up to 80%! With tables outlining the effective use of all your home appliances and recommendations for money-saving appliances, this book is a MUST for the budget-conscious household. 160 pp.; Rodale (paperback) **$9.95**

▲ **2542. Designing and Building a Solar House** Written by one of America's foremost authorities on solar architecture. It is a practical "how-to" guide that clearly demonstrates the most sensible ways to marry good house design with contemporary solar technology. Included is a thorough discussion of both "active" and "passive" solar systems, and even a listing of today's leading solar homes. 288 pp.; 400 illus.; Garden Way (paperback) **$15.95**

▼ **2610. The Backyard Builder** Here is a step-by-step guide for over 150 projects for the gardener and homeowner, accompanied by over 100 photos, 400 illustrations, materials lists and shopping guides. You are sure to find many useful, attractive projects that the entire family can help with. 656 pp.; Rodale (hardcover) **$21.95**

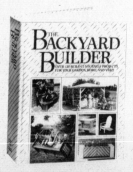

▲ **2606. Building Fences** With emphasis on function and style, this guide to a wide variety of fence-building is a solid how-to book. With easy-to-read instructions, and plenty of illustrations, this book is a must for the professional and the do-it-yourselfer. 188 pp.; Williamson Publishing (paperback) **$13.95**